The G
ELE
Maintenanᴄᴄ

John Whitfield

E·P·A
PRESS

Additional copies of this book should be available through any good bookshop. In case of difficulty please contact the publishers directly at:

E·P·A Press
Bulse Grange
Wendens Ambo
Saffron Walden, CB11 4JT

Tel: 01799 541207, Fax: 01799 541166

Pads of Electrical Installation, Minor Works and Periodic Inspection Certificates are available directly from the publishers at the above address.

Published by E·P·A Press, Wendens Ambo, UK

ISBN 0 9537885 2 0

The author and the publishers are grateful to the Institution of Electrical Engineers for permission to reproduce extracts from the 16th Edition of its Regulations for Electrical Installations. These Regulations are definitive and should always be consulted in their original form in case of doubt.

British Library Cataloguing in Publication Data
Whitfield, J.F. (Frederic), 1930 -

Designed by Geoffrey Wadsley
Printed in the United Kingdom by St Edmundsbury Press

Contents

Preface

Maintenance of electrical systems is not an option, it is essential.

Not only will proper maintenance keep the system concerned in good operating condition, it is also a legal requirement. The Health and Safety at Work Etc Act 1974 is concerned with safety, health, welfare at work and the control of dangerous substances and emissions into the atmosphere. It puts a duty on all concerned, both employers and employees, to ensure the safety, health and welfare of everyone who uses the premises and systems they contain. If this requirement is to be met, equipments and installations must not only be installed to comply with the requirements, they must also be maintained so that they continue to do so.

There is now a daunting list of requirements and of regulations that must be followed to ensure compliance with the Health and Safety at Work Act. These are listed and explained in Chapter 1. Throughout this book there is continual emphasis on the need to comply with the many regulations that now beset the maintenance manager. The cost of compliance with all of them will be onerous, but the system owner has no choice. They are the laws, and they must be obeyed.

This book has been written in response to many requests for a simplified, and, hopefully, a more understandable, overview of the requirements for electrical maintenance set out in the IEE publication 'Electrical Maintenance'. It does not try to explain basic electrical theory, or to enter in detail into the Requirements for Electrical Installations, BS 7671, (the IEE Wiring Regulations) or those of the Electrical Safety at Work Act. Books, which deal with some of these subjects, are listed below.

John Whitfield
Norwich

Acknowledgements

Dr. Katie Petty-Saphon, the Publisher, for her continued support and help.
Nat Hiller, the Editor, for his wise advice always.
My daughter, Lesley Weller, for her kindness and consideration.

Helpful publications

Electrical Craft Principles (two volumes) 4th edition, published by the
Institution of Electrical Engineers.
The Electrician's Guide to the IEE Wiring Regulations, 6th edition, published by
EPA Press.
The Guide to Electrical Safety at Work, 3rd edition, published by EPA Press

Important Notice

Throughout this Guide people are referred to in the masculine, i.e. always 'he' or
'him' and never 'she' or 'her'. It is accepted that an increasing number of women
are becoming involved with electrical maintenance and apologies are made to them
for the sole use of the masculine gender. It will be appreciated that to use both
genders throughout the text would lead to unnecessary complication. In this
respect, it is interesting to note that all of the Regulations and Codes of Practice
considered in this book use the masculine gender exclusively.

Abbreviations

Technical work is increasingly full of abbreviations, often with no explanation of their meaning. This section lists the abbreviations used in this book and gives the meanings.

Sometimes the abbreviations refer to an organisation. In such cases, as well as indicating the meaning, there is a brief note to describe the organisation itself.

ASTA   ASTA is an independent certification organisation for electrical products. Equipment carrying the ASTA Diamond Mark has been independently tested and approved as safe for its intended purpose.

BSI   The British Standards Institution. Founded in 1901, the Institution works through its committees to write the standards needed to increase efficiency and safety. The BSI carries out inspections and tests to ensure the safety and quality of products carrying its marks, such as the Kitemark and CE. It is the publisher, together with the IEE, of the Requirements for Electrical Installations, BS 7671, as well as numerous other standards with applications to electrical maintenance.

CCA   The CENELEC Certification Agreement covering equipment within the Low Voltage Directive, such as electro-domestic appliances, electronic appliances, and electrical installation material.

CE mark   If a manufacturer marks his product CE it indicates that he believes it to comply with the requirements of all the relevant European Standards. Testing may be carried out by the manufacturer or by an external test house, and the BSI may prosecute those who make false or unsubstantiated claims.

CECC mark   The CECC Mark is operated by the CECC System. It provides third party certification for electronic component characteristics and performance EN ISO 9001, 9002 and EN45001

CENELEC   The European Committee for Electrotechnical Standardisation. It was set up in 1973 as a non-profit making organisation under Belgian law. Its purpose is to harmonise standards throughout

Europe, to which end it works with 35,000 technical experts from 19 European countries. It works through a large number of Technical Committees (TCs) with precise titles and scopes to prepare the standards. It is not imperative that National bodies must accept the standards. For example, for many years continental countries have allowed the installation of socket outlets in bathrooms in compliance with their own standards, but such a practice will not comply with UK Requirements for Electrical Installations, BS 7671.

CECED   The European Committee of Manufacturers of Domestic Equipment.

CMS   Cable management systems.

EMC   Electromagnetic compatiblity.

EMI   Electromagnetic interference.

ESI   Electrostatic interference.

HSE   The Health and Safety Executive, whose purpose is to ensure that risks to people's health and safety from work activities are properly controlled. It works through the enforcement of the Health and Safety at Work Etc. Act, and its Regulations and Codes of Practice, many of those applying to maintenance being considered in Chapter 1.

HSC   The Health and Safety Commission is responsible to the government for the administration of the Health and Safety at Work Etc. Act throughout Great Britain. It also conducts and sponsors research, promotes training and provides an information and advisory service. The HSC oversees the work of the HSE and is free to delegate powers to it as it wishes.

IEE   The Institution (not Institute) of Electrical Engineers is the senior professional body for electrical engineers and has something over 130,000 members. Corporate members (Members and Fellows) are Chartered Engineers. The IEE was solely responsible for many years for the Regulations for Electrical Installations (commonly known as the 'Wiring Regs'), but in 1991 the BSI published BS 7671 (the 'Requirements for Electrical Installations') jointly with the IEE.

IEC   The International Electrotechnical Commission was founded in 1906. It is the world organisation for preparing and publishing international standards for all electrical, electronic and related technologies. Adoption of a standard is by voting amongst the fifty plus member countries, for each of whom its use is entirely voluntary.

ISO   The International Organisation for Standardisation is a world-
            wide federation of national standards bodies from one hundred
            and thirty counties. The organisation was established in 1947 to
            facilitate the international exchange of goods and services. It is
            responsible for many of the standards we take for granted, such as
            paper sizes, the marking of controls on cars, S I units, and so on.
            Adoption of an internationally agreed standard in a particular
            country is entirely voluntary.

KEYMARK agreement   The Keymark is a European quality mark designating
            conformity of any household or similar product with the require-
            ments of the corresponding standard. It was set up at the request
            of CECED.

KITEMARK This symbol is approved by the British Standards Institution
            (BSI) and indicates that the product concerned meets the relevant
            British, European or international standards, and is thus an indica-
            tion of quality and safety. It can only be displayed when the item
            marked has undergone stringent checks and testing..

LED   Light emitting diode.

NICEIC   National inspection council for electrical installation contracting.

PAT   Portable appliance tester.

PCB   Poly-Chlorinated Benzene. Was widely used as a coolant liquid in
            transformers and capacitors. Now outlawed because of its harmful
            effects on the environment.

RSI   Repetitive strain injury.

SI   The International System of Units.

SF_6 Sulphur Hexafluoride. Widely used as an arc-breaking medium in
            high voltage circuit breakers.

UPS   Uninterruptible power supply. When the normal supply fails, a
            UPS will take power from batteries or from a generator and invert
            it to take over the supply for a defined period of time.

Chapter 1

Why Do We Need Electrical Maintenance?

1.1 The need for maintenance

There are four major reasons why electrical maintenance is imperative. These are:

1 to make sure that the installation or equipment continues to operate efficiently,
2 to prevent the dangers that might arise in the event of failure,
3 to prevent the costs associated with failure, and
4 to minimise the environmental pollution which would occur if the by-products of maintenance (spent lamps, oil, devices containing PCBs, etc.) are not disposed of correctly.

The need for efficient operation is obvious. Prevention of dangers will be considered in the next section. Balancing the costs of reliable operation and of maintenance will be further considered in Chapter 2, whilst Chapter 13 deals with the disposal of hazardous waste.

1.2 Preventing danger

The common law of Great Britain imposes an obligation on every person to take care of his (or her) neighbour. The word neighbour, in this context, does not simply mean the person who lives next door. It means everybody with whom we come into contact or who are affected by anything that we do. If, for example we drive our motor vehicle dangerously, the common law is likely to be used to discipline us if, as a result, there is an accident.

In the same way, our actions at work can result in court action. If we fail correctly to maintain a machine so that it causes injury to a person, we are likely to be called to account. The fundamental legislation is the Health and Safety at Work Etc Act, passed in 1974. (It is believed that this is the only British law to have 'Etc' as part of its title). The Act gives power to the

Secretary of State to make any Regulations he considers to be necessary. It also gives the Health and Safety Commission the power to issue Codes of Practice, which detail the steps to be taken to ensure safe working.

The failure of a person to comply with a Code of Practice does not in itself render a person liable to civil or criminal prosecution. Such a failure, however, could be used as evidence in any court case resulting from an occurrence (such as an accident) which was the result of the failure.

There are many regulations and Codes of Practice which are concerned with maintenance. Some of the more important are considered in the next section.

1.3 Regulations and Codes of Practice

There are numerous Regulations and Codes of Practice, and continuing to be aware of them all and of their requirements is a daunting task. Ignorance of them is no defence in a court of law. It is thus imperative that the maintenance manager is fully aware of all of them.

1.3.1 The Health and Safety at Work Etc Act, 1974

Sections 2, 3 and 4 of the Act put a duty of care on the employer, the employee and the self-employed to ensure that all using the workplace have their safety, health and welfare protected. Section 6 requires that the designer, manufacturer or installer of systems makes sure that those who operate them have adequate information to ensure that use will be safe and not a risk to health. This requires that those who supply and install electrical systems and installations must not only test them before use to ensure their safety, but must also provide information which will allow them to be used and maintained in a safe condition. In the case of machinery, this will involve provision of handbooks giving full details of the equipment concerned. For electrical installations, it involves the provision of an operational manual, further details of which will be found in Chapter 4.

The Health and Safety at Work Act is the enabling legislation under which a whole range of Regulations and Codes of Practice are issued, including all of those detailed below.

1.3.2 The Electricity at Work Regulations, 1989

These Regulations (SI No. 635) impose duties on all employers, employees and self-employed persons to ensure that the safety requirements of the Regulations are met. These requirements may be summarised as:

1 All systems must be maintained so as to prevent danger so far as is reasonably practicable.

2 All systems must be manufactured, constructed and installed so as to prevent danger so far as is reasonably practicable.

3 All work on, or near, the system, must be carried out so as to prevent danger so far as is reasonably practicable.

4 All equipment provided for protecting people who work on or near the systems must be suitable for the use for which it was provided, be properly maintained and be properly used.

The word 'system' covers the complete electrical system, including the fixed installation as well as equipment connected to it, both permanently or via plugs and sockets. Also included are portable appliances, such as business and office equipment; the Institution of Electrical Engineers has published a Code of Practice for In-Service Inspection and Testing of Electrical Equipment. Fuller details of the requirements are given in Chapter 9.

As far as the electrical installation is concerned, the Electricity at Work Regulations advise that the work should comply with BS 7671, 'Requirements for Electrical Installations', almost universally called the 16th Edition of the IEE Wiring Regulations. An installation following BS 7671 is almost certain to achieve compliance with the Electricity at Work Regulations. However, the scope of the latter is wider than that of BS 7671 in that they require:

1 Installations are to be installed and constructed so as to be safe;

2 Installations are to be maintained so as to be safe;

3 Any equipment provided for work must be suitable for its purpose; and

4 Any work associated with the electrical installation must be carried out safely.

The Electricity at Work Regulations also require that the electrical installation shall be properly maintained, that staff shall be competent and properly trained, and that proper working practices and suitable equipment are used. A much more detailed study of the subject will be found in 'The Guide to Electrical Safety at Work', by John Whitfield, published by EPA Press.

1.3.3 Management of Health and Safety at Work Regulations, 1992

These Regulations are Approved Code of Practice L21. They require that every employer must make a proper assessment of the risks to health and safety of his employees whilst they are at work and of other persons (who are not his employees) arising out of the conduct of his operations.

The Electricity at Work Regulations deal specifically with hazards associated with electrical systems, whilst the Management Regulations are concerned with risk assessment in the broadest sense. They point to the need for health and safety training for staff, to make them competent to carry out their function. In many occupations this may well be the need for simple first aid training, whilst in more technical situations where more specialised knowledge is necessary, the employer must provide facilities for acquisition of such knowledge except where close supervision is provided by a skilled and competent person. The employer must make a proper assessment of the risks involved and significant findings must be recorded together with the control measures taken.

Employees are not exempt from the requirements of these Regulations. They must use machinery in accordance with their training and the instructions received, and are required to notify the employer if they have concerns as to the safety of their fellow employees or of the machinery they are operating. As far as maintenance is concerned, if an employee has doubts about his competence to complete the work assigned to him, he has a duty to notify his employer of this at once.

1.3.4 Personal Protective Equipment at Work Regulations, 1992

These Regulations are Approved Code of Practice L25. Every employer must ensure that suitable personal protective equipment is provided for the use of his employees. The nature of this equipment will, of course, vary depending on the work concerned, but must take account of environmental conditions, risks, ergonomic requirements, and the health of the person using it. It must fit the user properly and must comply with the appropriate standards. The protective equipment must be suitable for the task undertaken. For example, the type of insulating tools and gloves used for live line maintenance will depend on the voltage of the system concerned.

There is a requirement that employees should use the protective equipment provided in accordance with the training and instructions received. For example, it is not uncommon to witness the operator of a pneumatic road drill with his ear defenders hanging round his neck. It is no defence for him to claim that he has a right to damage his own hearing by not wearing the protection properly. The employer is right to take disciplinary action in such a case. Employees are required to report immediately the loss of or damage to protective equipment. The legislation requires that proper records should be kept of protective equipment and a system devised to ensure that employees still have the equipment and that it is in good order. The presence of such a system does not reduce the responsibility of the employee to report the loss of, or a defect in, his protective equipment.

1.3.5 Workplace (Health, Safety and Welfare) Regulations, 1992

These Regulations are Approved Code of Practice L24. Whilst the Health and Safety at Work Regulations are concerned with maintenance of the electrical system in a safe condition, they do not cover failures. The Workplace Regulations are concerned with the consequences of system and equipment failures. For example, the failure of an emergency lighting system may not, in itself, be an electrical hazard, but such a hazard may well exist due to its failure. The Workplace Regulations impose maintenance requirements on systems such as emergency lighting, escalators, moving walkways, fire alarms, powered doors and so on. They are, in fact, a good deal wider than the foregoing would suggest, covering also the maintenance of fences, devices to limit the opening of windows, equipment used for window cleaning and so on.

1.3.6 Manual Handling Operations Regulations, 1992

These Regulations are based on HSE Guidance L23. Employers are required to avoid the need for employees to carry out manual handling operations that involve the risk of injury. Where unavoidable, assessment must be made to reduce the risk as far as possible. The subject of manual handling is considered further in Chapter 15.

1.3.7 Health and Safety (Display Screen Equipment) Regulations, 1992

These Regulations are based on HSE Guidance L26. They cover the correct positioning of screens and of lighting to reduce the possible dangers of eye damage and of repetitive strain injury (RSI). The subject is further discussed in Chapter 8.

1.3.8 Construction (Design and Management) Regulations, 1994

These Regulations are based on HSE Guidance L54. They are concerned with construction work and will thus generally have little effect on electrical maintenance. A maintenance manager will need, however, to make sure that the construction design will facilitate, rather than hinder, maintenance operations. This may apply particularly to access for maintenance of lighting.

1.3.9 Health and Safety (Signs and Signals) Regulations, 1996

These Regulations are based on HSE Guidance L64. They detail the signs and signals required in the work place, and are considered in more detail in Chapter 16.

1.3.10 Fire Precautions (Work Place) Regulations, 1997

The Home Office and the Scottish Office have published 'Fire precautions in the work place', ISBN 0 1134 116 9. Its requirements are considered in detail in Chapter 6.

1.3.11 Provision and Use of Work Equipment Regulations, 1998

These Regulations are based on HSE Guidance L22. They are concerned with the construction and operation of work equipment, including that used specifically for maintenance. Such equipment is to be inspected after installation, before use, at suitable intervals during use and after exceptional circumstances, such as the operation of a circuit breaker under fault conditions. The guarding of dangerous machinery, provision of maintenance data and proper training for workers are also covered.

Chapter 2

Managing Electrical Maintenance

2.1 Types of Maintenance

There are three basic types of maintenance.

2.1.1 Preventive maintenance.

This maintenance is carried out before a breakdown or malfunction occurs with a view to preventing such failure. Usually such operations are planned and carried out regularly and at specified intervals, although sometimes they will be initiated as a result of measurements or observation of the operation concerned. An example of preventive maintenance is the routine changing of lamps in general factory lighting as they approach the end of their expected life.

2.1.2 Breakdown maintenance

Using this system, maintenance is only undertaken when the equipment concerned ceases to operate as expected. Perhaps the simplest example is the replacement of filament lamps in the home. We are not likely to change all our lamps at regular intervals (preventative maintenance), but only do so individually in the event of failure. The method is not likely to be appropriate for a large industrial undertaking where the loss of production as a result of breakdown may be significant.

2.1.3 Condition monitored maintenance

This method requires the manual or automatic monitoring of such factors as bearing and winding temperatures, vibration, lighting or electric current levels, and so on. The results will point to the need for a shutdown to enable maintenance to be carried out, rather than waiting for a breakdown, which may have far-reaching consequences in terms of safety and/or of cost.

2.2   Inspection and Testing

The purpose of inspection and testing is to discover if maintenance and repairs are required in the system concerned. The results of tests will show, when compared with earlier test results, if there has been a deterioration or a sudden change in the operation of the equipment, and thus if maintenance is required.

The question immediately arises as to how frequently such inspections and tests are required. In most cases, the legislation is of little help here, the only specified periods between inspections and tests being for electrical installations where public safety is concerned, such as places of entertainment, petrol filling stations, etc. The following tables 2.1 to 2.3 provide guidance to the intervals between electrical inspection and testing.

Table 2.1 lists the suggested periods between inspections and testing of electrical installations. The data for this Table is based on IEE Guidance Note 3, Inspection and Testing.

2.3   Safety procedures

The Health and Safety Executive has issued an Approved Code of Practice L21, entitled 'Management of Health and Safety at Work Regulations, 1992'. The basic purpose of the Act is that employers must assess the risks to the health and safety of employees whilst at work, as well as to others who are not employees, but arising out of the work being carried out. The Code provides guidance on the assessment of these risks.

The management of maintenance is assisted by making sure that the process takes the following steps:

2.3.1   Policy statement

A policy statement indicating the company's commitment to health and safety should be drafted and signed by senior management.

Notes to Table 2.1(*opposite*)
1.   Care must be taken to comply with the Electricity Supply Regulations, SI no. 1057
2.   Care must be taken to comply with the Electricity at Work Regulations, SI no. 635
3.   See BS 5266 Part 1 Code of Practice for Emergency Lighting at other than places of entertainment.
4.   Batteries and generators have other recommended testing intervals
5.   See BS 5839 part 1
6.   Local Authority licence conditions also apply
7.   See SI no. 1129 (clause 27), the Cinematography (Safety) Regulations.

Table 2.1 Recommended Frequencies of Inspection and Testing of Electrical Installations

Type of installation	Maximum interval between inspections and tests	Routine check every	Note (see page 8 below left)
General installations			
Domestic	10 years or at tenancy change	——	
Commercial	5 years or at tenancy change	1 year	1, 2
Educational establishment	5 years	4 months	1, 2
Hospitals	5 years	1 year	1, 2
Industrial	3 years	1 year	1, 2
Residential accommodation	5 years	1 year or at occupancy change	1
Offices	5 years	1 year	1, 2
Shops	5 years	1 year	1, 2
Laboratories	5 years	1 year	1, 2
Special installations			
Emergency lighting	3 years	Daily/monthly	2, 3, 4
Fire alarms	1 year	Daily/weekly/monthly	2, 4, 5
Launderettes	1 year	1 year	1, 2, 6
Petrol filling stations	1 year	1 year	1, 2, 6
Construction site installations	3 months	3 months	1, 2
External installations			
Agricultural and horticultural	3 years	1 year	1,2
Caravans	3 years	1 year	
Caravan parks	1 year	6 months	1, 2, 6
Highway power supplies	6 years	As convenient	
Marinas	1 year	4 months	1, 2
Fish farms	1 year	4 months	1, 2
Buildings with access to the public			
Cinemas	1 year	4 months	2, 6, 7
Churches	5 years	1 year	2
Leisure complexes	1 year	4 months	1, 2, 6
Places of public entertainment	1 year	4 months	1, 2. 6
Restaurants and hotels	5 years	1 year	1, 2
Theatres	1 year	4 months	2, 6, 7
Public houses	5 years	1 year	1, 2, 6
Village halls	5 years	1 year	1,2

Table 2.2   Legal Maintenance Requirements

Installation type	Inspection frequency	Legislation
Lifts	6 monthly	Factories Act 1961 Offices Shops and Railway Premises (Lift and Hoist) Regulations 1968 Lifting Plant and Equipment Regulations 1992
Electrically operated hoist blocks	Every 14 months	Factories Act 1961 Construction (Lifting Operations) Regulations 1961
Cranes (jib, mobile, overhead travelling)	Every 14 months and after alteration or repair	Factories Act 1961 Construction (Lifting Operations) Regulations 1961
Cinema electrical installations	Annually	Cinematography Act 1909

Table 2.2 lists some of the electrical maintenance details required by the various Regulations. It is a legal requirement for this maintenance to be completed at periods no longer than those listed in the column headed 'Inspection frequency'.

2.3.2   Risk determination

Using the Code of Practice as guidance, an assessment must be made of the risks to health and to safety to workers and to others. Following the assessment must come decisions as to how the risks are to be managed.

2.3.3   Responsibilities

The responsibilities of individuals for safety must be clearly defined, as must be the final responsibility for implementing the safety policy of the company.

2.3.4   Control measures

The risks identified must be properly addressed. This is likely to involve a number of steps, which could include:

a) Changes of procedure
b) Issuing instructions
c) Purchase of equipment
d) Issuing of equipment to staff
e) Staff training
f) Control system to ensure that the policy is implemented
g) Information feedback to ensure that the policy is working

Table 2.3   Maintenance requirements

System	Task	Recommended Minimum Frequency	Reason for maintenance
General electrical equipment	Inspection and testing	See Chapter 9	Electricity at Work Regulations, 1989
Emergency lighting	See Chapter 7	See Chapter 7	Fire Precautions Act, 1971 Workplace (Health, Safety and Welfare)Regulations, 1992
Fire and alarm systems	See Chapter 6	See Chapter 6	Fire Precautions Act, 1971 Workplace (Health, Safety and Welfare)Regulations, 1992
Overhead travelling cranes and runways	Check all electrical equipment	3 monthly	Section 27, Factories Act, 1961
Refrigeration systems	Clean and disinfect reservoirs and pipes	6 monthly or on restarting after non-use for a month	HSE Guidance Booklet HS(G)70
Air conditioning systems	Test water quality and loss	Weekly	HSE Guidance Booklet HS(G)70
Personnel in cold rooms	Check door systems	3 monthly	Factories Act 1961 Electricity at Work Act 1989

In some cases the various Regulations are not specific concerning the periods between maintenance. Table 2.3 lists the minimum periods that are likely to be necessary. It must be appreciated that in the event of an accident, the plant operator will need to produce maintenance records, which show that the plant concerned has been properly and regularly maintained.

2.3.5 Safety Instructions
Written safety instructions will reduce doubts concerning responsibilities. They will also impress on management that they are ultimately responsible for compliance with the instructions, as well as the need for safety training. See 2.4 below.

2.3.6 Training
Training must be provided for all employees so that they can carry out the

specified safety instructions. The safety instructions themselves should point to the need for additional training if it becomes necessary.

2.3.7 Equipment

The safety instructions should ensure that staff make proper use of the correct equipment, notifying management when repair or replacement becomes necessary.

2.4   Electrical Safety Instructions

Only staff who are competent to do so should be allowed to work on any part of an electrical installation. Those who do so must be issued with safety instructions that have been discussed with them and agreed by them. Formal issue and receipt of these instructions may be used as an indication of competence.

Typical electrical safety instructions will include the following:

1 Details of the organisations concerned, of the senior manager or director responsible for safety, and of the competent person who is required to carry out the work in question.
2 Details of the possible dangers incurred when undertaking the work, such as fire, electric shock, burns, etc.
3 Clear indication of the notices, both cautionary and danger, which must be displayed.
4 Adequate information concerning the system on which work is to be carried out, together with the possible dangers involved.
5 Clear indication of the work to be carried out.
6 In the event of doubt, the worker should be encouraged to take up the matter with his superior.

The employee should sign to indicate receipt of the instructions. In the event that he objects to the instructions or to the work he is required to carry out, the person issuing the instructions must have the matter investigated, if necessary by a higher authority, before proceeding. All accidents or dangerous occurrences must be reported and properly investigated.

All employees must comply with these safety instructions, and must do so using safe working methods and the protective equipment and clothing provided for their safety. All employees who receive safety instructions must:

1 Fully understand the extent and nature of the work to be completed

2 Read the safety instructions and confirm to their superior that they are understood

3 Make sure that the work is carried out in complete accordance with the instructions

4 When in charge of the operation, provide all the supervision required.

2.5   Working on 'Dead' systems

It is of vital importance to make sure that the system in question really is dead, and that it remains so for the whole of the time during which the work is continued. The precautions to be taken before commencing work will include the following:

1 Open all circuit breakers and isolating switches, remove fuses and so on. Post warning notices at all such places to prohibit reclosing the electrical supply. This may present problems when workers may not be able to read English.

2 The circuits concerned must be proved dead by the use of a voltage testing device which is itself tested before and after use.

3 Take other steps to ensure that the supply will not be inadvertently reconnected. To this end, one or more of the following precautions should be taken:

a) all fuses removed , together with other current limiting devices, to be retained safely by the person responsible for the work

b) all switches and isolators opened must be locked off with approved locking devices, the keys being kept in a special key safe or by the person responsible for the work

c) where portable appliances are concerned and made dead by removal of a plug from a socket, some means must be devised to prevent re-insertion of the plug.

4 Some circuits are controlled by time switches and are dead during the 'off' period. On no account must the workers rely on the integrity of such a switch.

5 If exposed live conductors are present in the working area, they must be clearly identified by warning notices, which are clear to all workers. Where such live conductors are present, they should be screened from the workers.

2.6 Live Working

Regulation 14 of the Electricity at Work Regulations 1989 makes it clear that working on a live electrical system must **NOT** take place unless:

1 it is unreasonable in the circumstances for it to be dead, and
2 it is reasonable in the circumstances for live working to take place, and
3 suitable precautions are taken to prevent injury, including the provision of special protective equipment

Live working, including testing and fault finding, should only be attempted when there is no other way of carrying out the work. The method is routinely used in many circumstances, notably when working on high voltage or low voltage supply systems. It is usual in such cases for those carrying out the work to be especially competent and practised.

Testing and fault finding on electrical systems often cannot be carried out if the supply is disconnected. For example, measurement of earth fault loop impedance includes the supply system, which must remain connected. In such cases, not only must the tester take great care, but must ensure that the instruments and connecting leads he uses are of the right type for safe working.

2.7 The 'Permit-to-Work' System

An excellent method of reducing or removing the dangers of working on electrical systems is the adoption of the 'permit-to-work' system. It is based on the fact that we are all more careful if we know that we will be blamed for our wrong actions. No work may be started until the person who is to perform it is in possession of a permit-to-work, showing precisely what is to be done and where it is safe to work. A suitably competent engineer issues the permit after making certain that the work will be safe because he has switched off the electrical supplies to the area concerned, earthed live conductors and so on.

The permit is in duplicate, the top copy being given to the person who is to complete the work, who signs the second copy to indicate the date and time of its receipt. On completion of the work, he signs the top copy, confirming that the work is complete and that all those who report to him have been informed that the situation is again dangerous. The original is destroyed, but the copy is retained. In the event of an accident the system shows precisely what happened, and what instructions were given, so that any blame can be clearly apportioned to the person responsible.

When described, it sounds as if the system exists to punish the guilty. In fact, the result is that accidents seldom happen, because all concerned know that they will be held to account for errors or omissions. In the event of an accident, the system makes analysis of events much simpler, allowing changes in procedures that will prevent a reoccurrence.

Permits to work will vary somewhat depending on the situations in which they are used. A typical example follows.

PERMIT-TO-WORK (front)

Serial number ....

Issued to .... in charge of the work

I hearby declare that the following apparatus is dead, isolated from all live conductors, and is connected to earth.

The system is isolated at the following points. ....

Caution notices have been posted at ....

Safety locks have been fitted at ....

The work to be carried out is ....

....

Diagram

Signed by ....

Name in block capitals ....

Time .... Date ....

Receipt
I accept responsibility for carrying out the work on the system detailed in this permit-to-work and no attempt will be made by me or by persons under my control to work on other systems.

Signed by ....

Name in block capitals ....

Time .... Date ....

PERMIT-TO-WORK (back)

Clearance.
The work for which this permit was issued is now completed/suspended *
and all persons under my charge have been withdrawn and warned that it is
no longer safe to work on the system covered by this permit.

The work is complete/incomplete*.

All gear and tools have/have not* been removed.

*delete the words not applicable, and where necessary state:

Abnormalities are at

....

....

Additional earths are at

....

....

Signed by ....

Name in block capitals ....

Time .... Date ....

Cancellation
This permit to work is cancelled.

Signed by ....

Name in block capitals ....

Time .... Date ....

Chapter 3

Maintaining Electrical Installations

3.1 The need for maintenance

The prevention of danger to users from faulty electrical installations is the subject of Regulation 4(2) of the Electricity at Work Regulations, 1989. The subsequent Regulation 4(3) is concerned with carrying out the maintenance safely. How regularly the installation should be inspected is a matter for the judgement of the responsible manager (see Section 3.2 below), but it should be remembered that in the event of an accident, maintenance records will be examined and possibly criticised.

Systems requiring maintenance will include the electrical distribution arrangements, the electrical installation, as well as all appliances and equipments fed from it. It must be appreciated that the term 'electrical equipment' means any equipment using electrical energy, including battery-powered equipment. It may seem that the danger of battery powered appliances is non-existent, but we must remember that modern electronic inversion systems are capable of producing very high voltage outputs from low voltage inputs. Additionally, there is a severe fire danger due to the misuse (such as short-circuiting) of high-powered battery systems, like those often in use for uninterruptible powers supplies (UPSs).

The electrical installation itself will need to comply with BS 7671, 'Requirements for Electrical Installations' (almost universally known as the 16th Edition of the IEE Wiring Regulations). The necessary test procedures for such installations are considered later in this Chapter. The in-service inspection of other electrical equipments and appliances is discussed in Chapter 9.

3.2 How often do we need to inspect and test?

This matter is covered in Section 2.2 of Chapter 2. It is important to appreciate that the Electrical Installation Certificate, which must be provided after every inspection and test, will also include a clear recommendation of when the next series should be carried out. Table 2.1 suggests suitable test intervals for various types of installation. Experience, and a careful examination of test results, will show if these periods should be extended or shortened. It must be remembered that after an accident, the responsible manager will need to justify any changes made.

3.3 Managing inspection and testing

A very important aspect of managing inspection and testing has been covered in the previous Section. It is clearly of paramount importance to ensure that an electrical installation is inspected and tested frequently enough to make it unlikely that a dangerous fault will occur between tests and inspections. In some cases (for example, the ten-year period for a domestic installation) the interval between inspections and tests assumes that the user will draw attention to faults and will have them properly corrected. A main purpose of the regime is to identify deterioration of the installation so that remedial work can be carried out, which, in some cases will be needed to bring the installation up to modern standards.

Routine checks, sometimes on a daily basis, will sometimes be necessary, especially where the general public uses the installation. Such routine checks will not necessarily need to be carried out by electrically qualified staff. A responsible person can carry them out and report defects to others who are qualified to rectify them. A record must be kept of such defects, with clear indication that they have been corrected speedily.

The daily inspection will look for the following items:

- wear
- deterioration
- missing items, such as screws and covers
- broken equipment or parts
- overheating and its signs
- properly secured doors and covers on electrical enclosures
- obstructions to switchgear
- loose fixings
- proper labelling

As well as a visual inspection, it would be sensible on a daily basis to carry out the following operations where they are appropriate. Clearly, to switch off a system whose operation is essential would not be sensible.

- switch equipment on and off
- press the test button on each RCD
- operate switchgear

3.4 Periodic Inspection and Testing

The steps to be taken here are specified in Chapter 73 of BS 7671, 'Requirements for Electrical Installations'. They state that:

'Inspection comprising careful scrutiny of the installation shall be carried out, without dismantling, or with partial dismantling as required, supplemented by testing to verify compliance with Sections 731 and 732 and as far as possible to provide for:

1 The safety of persons and livestock against the effects of electric shock and burns, and

2 Protection against damage to property by fire and heat arising from installation defect, and

3 The assurance that the installation is not damaged or deteriorated so as to impair safety, and

4 The identification of installation defects or non-compliance with the Regulations which may give rise to danger.'

A major plank of the periodic inspection system is just that. Inspection. Tests will indicate the presence of faults or of deterioration, but they are no substitute for a detailed and expert visual inspection, which, in some circumstances, will bring to light hazards not apparent from the test results. An example concerns missing or damaged insulation. In some cases this will not result in a low insulation resistance reading, but may result in live conductors being open to touch with the consequent danger of electric shock.

The tests required by Sections 731 and 732 of BS 7671 would allow production of the Schedule of Test Results that must accompany the Periodic Inspection Report. They include the following:

1 Continuity tests, to be carried out between all main bonding connections and all supplementary bonding connections. It is very important that protective and bonding conductors are NOT disconnected when the main supply cannot be isolated for operational reasons

2 Polarity tests, to ensure that the phase and neutral conductors have not become transposed. The test must be carried out:

a) at the origin of the installation

b) at all socket outlets

c) at 10% of switches and other control devices

d) at 10% of all centre-contact lampholders.

In the event of finding a failure in polarity, the part of the installation concerned must be retested with the proportion of items tested under (c) and (d) above being increased to 25%. If a further fault is found the complete installation must be retested.

3 Earth fault loop impedance tests, to ensure the correct operation of protective devices (fuses and circuit breakers) in the event of an earth fault. The test must be repeated:

a) at the origin of the installation

b) at each distribution board

c) either at every socket outlet or at the end of every radial circuit.

It should be noted that the majority of earth fault loop test instruments will trip RCDs. If this happens, either:-

i) the value of R1 + R2 is measured during the continuity test (item 1 above) and added to the external fault loop impedance Ze measured at the mains intake position , or

ii) the test is carried out with the RCDs short circuited. If this method is used, it is very important to remove the short circuiting connections after the tests.

4 Insulation resistance tests of all cables in the installation, with all protective devices in place and with all switches closed. Where there is two-way or intermediate switching, the test is carried out with switches in all possible operating positions. It is important to note that the high voltage used for insulation resistance testing will damage electronic devices such as electronic starter switches for discharge lamps, passive infra-red detectors, lamp dimmers, and so on. Where such items are present, the test should be carried out between protective conductors and phase and neutral conductors connected together. A test between phase and neutral conductors will damage the vulnerable devices in question.

5 Functional tests to verify the correct operation of the installation. These will include:

a) operation of all isolating and switching devices,

b) verification of all interlocking devices

c) the correct operation of all RCDs. This can be carried out by operation of the test button, by simulation of a fault with a 15-

watt filament lamp connected from phase to earth, or by a dedicated RCD tester.

d) checking the presence and condition of all required labels
e) switching of all manually-operated circuit breakers
f) injection testing of all suitably-equipped circuit breakers.

Technical explanations of these tests will be found in Chapter 4.

The final Periodic Inspection Report will include schedules of the inspection and of the test results. It is very important that the person carrying out the test compares his results with those of the previous test to bring to light changes in test results. In this way, early warning of possible future faults can often be deduced.

Where the inspection and test reveals a possibly dangerous installation, the tester should at once report this to the owner or operator, stressing, if necessary, the need for prompt remedial action. In the event of a refusal to address a dangerous situation, the tester may consider calling in the Health and Safety Executive, who may serve a Prohibition Notice, requiring that the installation be shut down until it is made safe. Alternatively, they may issue an Improvement Notice, which specifies that action must be taken within a given period. Such activity is unlikely to endear the tester to the installation operator, but may well avert a dangerous situation.

Chapter 4

Testing Electrical Installations

4.1 The need for testing and for special test instruments

Testing of new electrical installations is a requirement of BS 7671, as is regular testing throughout the life of the installation to ensure its safety and efficiency. Testing is also a requirement when an electrical installation is extended or modified, even if the change is as minor as the repositioning of a lighting switch. Such tests are considered in this Chapter, but very detailed information will be found in IEE Guidance Note 3 to BS 7671, 'Inspection and Testing'.

The correct testing of electrical installations demands the possession of a number of very specialist pieces of test equipment. Whilst the insulation resistance tester (commonly, but not entirely correctly, referred to as the 'Megger') has become widespread, special items such as the earth fault loop impedance tester, the residual current device (RCD) tester and the earth electrode tester are also required. All of these specialist instruments can be included in one testing device. Another innovation is the presence in instruments of internal memories, so that the equipment will 'remember' test results for later downloading to a computer with a suitable program. Test results can only be relied upon if the accuracy of the test equipment is verified. The required limits and the need for calibration are considered in section 4.9.

Testing can be a very dangerous activity if the correct safety rules are not obeyed. It is important for most tests that the electrical supply to an installation should be switched off (and becomes 'dead') before testing commences. There are exceptions to this rule. Earth fault loop testing can only be carried out on a 'live' installation because the supply system forms an important part of the circuits being tested. Again, RCDs can only be tested if the supply is present, because it is necessary to allow them to operate. Quite clearly, tests of these types on energised installations require the greatest care and should only be carried out by experienced testing personnel.

4.2 Testing continuity

These tests ensure that the conductor system under test is continuous and will be capable of carrying electrical current if required to do so. They are carried out with an ohmmeter, which passes current through the test system and computes the resistance from measurements of this current and of the voltage needed to drive it. Harmonisation of CENELEC document HD 384.6.61 SI with BS 7671 means that continuity testers must be capable of providing a test current of not less than 200 mA and a no-load voltage of between 4 V and 24 V. The technical need for the specified current is not altogether clear, since a current of this value will not stress the connections or conductor more than will a lower value.

The conductors whose continuity is required will probably extend for a long distance. Quite clearly the test instrument cannot be at both ends of the system at the same time, so a return conducting path becomes a necessity. There are two ways in which this can be provided.

4.2.1 Applying a temporary short circuiting link at the fuse board.

This method is illustrated by Fig 4.1. The link is made between either the neutral and earth or the phase and earth, the chosen live conductor (neutral or phase) forming the return lead. Measurement from the far end of the circuit from the fuseboard (a socket is shown in Fig 4.1) will give the combined resistances of the live and protective conductors. Should the exact resistance of either one be required, this can be calculated using the formula:

$$R_p = R \times \frac{A_{ph}}{A_p + A_{ph}}$$

where R_p is the resistance of the required conductor
R is the measured resistance
A_{ph} is the c.s.a. of the phase conductor
A_p is the c.s.a. of the protective conductor

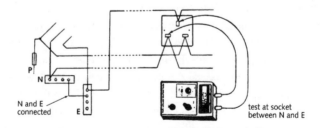

Fig. 4.1 Continuity test of a protective conductor using the neutral as a return.

The calculation will only be correct if both phase and protective conductors are made of the same material, but since most conductors are of copper this is seldom a problem. Quite clearly, if the protective system is composed in whole or in part of ferrous metal (conduit, trunking, armouring, etc.) this formula should not be used.

It is of the **greatest importance** that the short circuiting link inserted for testing purposes is removed as soon as the test is completed. There may be some weight in the argument that the link should be from the phase to the protective conductor. If this is the case and the link is not removed, switching on will result in an earth fault which will cause the fuse or circuit breaker to operate, thus detecting the failure. If a link is left in place from neutral to earth, the fault may go undetected.

4.2.2 Using a wander lead

This test is similar to that above, but the return lead is not one of the installation conductors. It is a test lead which is long enough to stretch from the test point (perhaps a socket) to the fuseboard. If required, the resistance of this wander lead may be measured and subtracted from the total resistance measurement to give the true resistance for the conductor under test.

If the test system is made up of ferrous material, (steel conduit, trunking, etc.) the tester must use his discretion before accepting a result obtained by measurement with either of the above methods. The system under test should be inspected to verify its soundness, and if in doubt should be further tested using a special ohmmeter which will apply at least 1.5 times the circuit design current, with a maximum of 25 A.

4.3   Testing insulation resistance

BS 7671 requires that insulation should be tested for 230/400 V systems using an applied voltage of 500 V. The test instrument must be capable of maintaining that voltage when the current load is 1 mA. As insulation resistance becomes lower and so the current from the instrument increases, and the maximum current will correspond with the minimum value of insulation resistance. The minimum acceptable value of insulation resistance accepted by BS 7671 is 0.5 MΩ, the resistance value that will draw a current of 1 mA from a 500 V source. The required test voltages and minimum insulation resistances to comply with BS 7671 are shown in Table 4.1.

Table 4.1   Minimum values of test voltage and of installation resistance

Circuit nominal voltage (V)	d.c. test voltage (V)	Minimum insulation resistance (MΩ)
Safety and protective extra-low voltage (SELV & PELV)	250	0.25
Up to 500 V except for SELV & PELV, but including FELV (functional extra-low voltage)	500	0.5
Above 500 V	1000	1.0

We find a strange anomaly here. Whilst 0.5 MΩ is acceptable according to BS 7671, it is a very low value for a healthy electrical installation, and it is suggested by IEE Guidance Note 3 that levels below 2 MΩ require further investigation. The National Inspection Council for Electrical Installation Contracting (NICEIC) suggests that the minimum acceptable level is 5 MΩ. Probably the practical electrician should work on the latter figure, at least for an individual circuit. The more circuits that are added in parallel, the lower the resistance will become, so that for a large installation the insulation resistance can become very low indeed, even though the installation is entirely healthy. For this reason, a large installation may be sub-divided before testing, for example by testing each distribution board separately.

Separate tests must be completed between all live conductors (phase and neutral for a single-phase supply and between phases and from each phase to neutral for a three-phase supply). In addition, tests must be carried out from all live conductors connected together (phase(s) and neutral) to earth. When carrying out periodic tests, the cables should be visually inspected to verify their condition. However, it does not follow that perished insulation will always result in a low insulation resistance reading.

It is MOST IMPORTANT for the tester to appreciate that a modern installation is likely to have a number of electronic devices connected to it, such as fluorescent tube starters, passive infra-red detectors, alarms, lighting dimmers and so on. They may be connected from phase to neutral or from phase to earth. During normal operation on a single-phase supply they will thus have the full 230 V (in practice often exceeding 240 V) supply connected across them, and they will be designed to withstand this voltage. However, it is quite common for electronic component failure to occur if they are subjected to the 500 V or 1000 V supply used as standard for insulation resistance testing. Such devices must therefore be found and disconnected before testing, care being taken to reconnect them afterwards.

Insulation resistance is a much more complex subject than is generally realised. It is affected by factors such as age, heat, vibration, moisture, oil, corrosive substances, contamination and so on. Possibly contamination by water is most important, but factors such as the weather, the temperature of the system under test, and how recently it has been used will affect readings. We normally use a direct voltage for insulation resistance testing, because the insulation of the conductors behaves as a dielectric, so that there is capacitance in the system. An alternating voltage would result in a steady capacitive current through the insulation, affecting the reading obtained. This is avoided by using a direct voltage, but we must remember that there will still be a capacitive current whilst the conductor system charges up. For this reason, test readings must not be taken too quickly after the test button is operated (five seconds is a reasonable delay). Similarly, it must be appreciated that the system under test will charge up to the test voltage during testing, and must be discharged afterwards. The charge will dissipate by normal leakage, but this may take up to twenty seconds, although most insulation resistance testers are arranged to short-circuit the test conductors so that the charge is dispelled on completion of the test.

Some specialist insulation resistance testers have a guard terminal. It can be used to offset the effect of leakage over the surface of the insulation at the cable ends, and thus to give a more accurate reading.

4.4   Testing Polarity

To reduce the possibility of electric shock, it is important that all single-pole switches and all protective devices (fuses and circuit breakers) are connected in the phase (unearthed) conductor rather than in the earthed neutral conductor. It is thus important to verify that the polarity of an installation is correct, or this vital safeguard may be lost.

The test is carried out using an ohmmeter and a long wander lead as indicated in Fig 4.2.

An alternative to the use of the wander lead, which is often awkward to use, will be to make a temporary connection from the phase to the protective (earth) conductor system at the mains position. The ohmmeter can

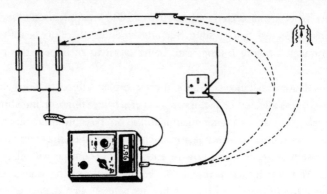

Fig. 4.2 Polarity test with a wander lead.

then be used between phase and protective conductor to verify polarity. It is of vital importance to remove the temporary phase/earth connection at the completion of the test. Most phase-earth loop testers and RCD testers are equipped with neon indicators to confirm correct polarity. For periodic testing (when the supply is already connected) it is common to use a neon tester to verify the presence of voltage at switches and sockets. This method must be used with care, both from the safety point of view and because spurious indications are possible.

One practical method of testing socket outlets is to connect two low-power indicator lamps to a plug. One is connected from phase to neutral, and the other from phase to earth. If both light when the plug is inserted into a live socket, this will indicate both correct polarity and the continuity of live conductors. With this method it is very important to use very low power indicator lamps if the circuit under test is protected by an RCD. The lowest power filament lamp will pass enough current to earth to trip the RCD. The alternative is to use neon indicators, or light emitting diodes with suitable series-connected resistors.

4.5 Earth-fault Loop Impedance Testing

The measurement of earth-fault loop impedance, with a check against tables of values given in BS 7671, is essential if we are to be sure that the circuit protective device (fuse or circuit breaker) will operate in the event of an earth fault. The highest levels of loop impedance will always occur at the extremities of the installation where the cable lengths that contribute to the impedance are longest. It is at these extremities that testing is most important. The test cannot be performed until the supply is connected, because the impedance of the supply itself forms part of the loop.

The earth-fault loop tester is a dedicated instrument. In simple principle (see Fig 4.3) it connects a resistor (typically of 10 Ω) between the phase and earth for a very short period, usually not exceeding two cycles of the supply (40 ms for a 50 Hz supply). A current, usually greater than 20 A will flow, the value depending on the loop impedance. The value of this current is measured and can be used to compute the loop impedance.

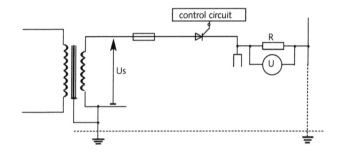

Fig. 4.3   Simplified principle of operation of the earth fault loop tester.

This phase-earth current will trip an RCD if fitted. It is thus important that RCDs are short-circuited before the test is performed, and even more important that the short circuits are removed after the test. Some manufacturers claim to have developed a system allowing the test to be performed without tripping RCDs. In some cases it would seem that this is achieved by limiting the loop current to less than the minimum 30 mA tripping current of the RCD. Such a low current test does not comply with the requirements of BS 7671.

If connected from phase to neutral the loop tester will carry the short circuit current of the system for a very short time. Some versions of the tester are arranged so that they will give a reading of the value of this current. The reading is of doubtful use, because the main purpose of a knowledge of short circuit current is to choose protective devices with a sufficiently high fault current breaking capacity. This process must, of course, be decided before the installation is complete, whilst the measurement described above can only be carried out when the supply has been connected. In practice, it is probably better to obtain the value of the short circuit current from the Electricity Supply Company. A problem here may be that these suppliers will often cover themselves against future reinforcement of their systems by quoting very high values. Table 4.2 provides data from which the prospective short circuit current may be estimated from the length and size of the supply cable.

Table 4.2 Estimation of prospective short circuit current (PSC)

Length of supply cable (m)	PSC for up to 25 mm² Al or 16 mm² Cu supply cable (kA)	PSC for over 35 mm² Al or 25 mm² Cu supply cable (kA)
5	10.0	12.0
10	7.8	9.3
15	6.0	7.4
20	4.9	6.2
25	4.1	5.3
30	3.5	4.6
40	2.7	3.6
50	2.0	3.0

NB 'Al' is the standard abbreviation for aluminium, and 'Cu' for copper.

4.6 Testing Earth Electrodes

The earth electrode is a means of making contact with the general mass of earth. In modern installations it is perhaps more usual for the Supply Company to provide an earth terminal at their incoming mains position, this terminal usually being connected to the armouring of the supply cable. Where an electrode is used, it must be tested to ensure that it makes good contact with earth. The consideration here is to ensure that the potential difference between the general mass of earth and the protective conductor system of the installation will never exceed 50 V for normal installations, or 25 V for construction sites and agricultural situations.

Where an RCD is used, it follows that the operating current of the device (usually not less than 30 mA) in amperes multiplied by the electrode resistance in ohms should not exceed 50 or 25. This leads to a maximum electrode resistance of 1667 Ω for normal installations or 833 Ω for construction sites and agricultural situations. In fact, BS 7430, Code of Practice for Earthing, recommends that the value should never exceed 100 Ω.

The test of the electrode is carried out using a special four-terminal tester. Before testing, all bonding conductors must be disconnected from the electrode to ensure that the measured resistance is truly that of the electrode alone. Care must be taken to reconnect the bonding conductors on completion of the test.

To carry out the test, a temporary electrode (Y) must be driven into the ground at a distance from the electrode under test depending on the situation, but usually between 30 m and 50 m. A second test electrode (Z) is positioned halfway between the electrode under test (X) and the test electrode (Y). The instrument is connected as shown in Fig 4.4, leads from P_1 and C_1 to X being combined into a single connection if their resistance is negligible. The resistance reading is then taken.

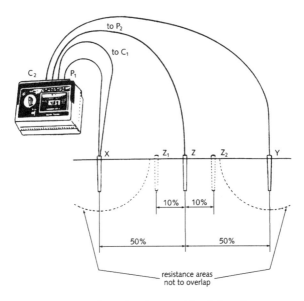

Fig. 4.4   Measurement of earth electrode resistance with a dedicated tester.

To ensure that the resistance areas of the two outer electrodes do not overlap, the test is repeated twice more with electrode Z placed 10% of distance X to Y on either side of its original position. If all readings are the same, this is the required electrode resistance. If the readings differ, the resistance areas do overlap and the whole test must be repeated with electrode Y placed further away from the electrode under test.

To measure the earth electrode resistance of an electrode used in conjunction with a domestic installation protected by an RCD, an earth fault loop impedance tester may be used. It is connected as shown in Fig 4.5. The resulting reading will actually include the supply impedance, but

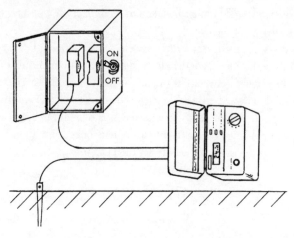

Fig. 4.5   Measurement of earth electrode resistance using an earth fault loop impedance tester.

will usually be accurate enough for its purpose. The displayed reading will, of course, always exceed the electrode resistance, so the error will be on the safe side.

4.7   Testing Residual Current Devices (RCDs)

All RCDs that comply with BS 4293 are provided with a test button. A test using this button WILL NOT satisfy the requirements of BS 7671 – it is provided so that the user can check regularly to ensure that the device is operational.

The test requires a dedicated RCD tester, which is connected between the phase and protective conductors on the load side of the RCD. Fig 4.6 shows the instrument plugged in to a socket for the test. If there are no sockets, the instrument can be connected to phase and earth using the leads usually provided with the tester. A selected value of current passes from the phase to earth, thus tripping the RCD, when the instrument displays the time taken to trip. This time will usually be between 10 and 20 ms, except for time delayed (S-type) RCDs.

For normal RCDs the trip time must measure less than 200 ms when the rated tripping current is applied for not more than 2 s. In the special case of an RCD which is intended to provide supplementary protection from direct contact, a current of 150 mA must trip the device within 40 ms. The RCD should NOT trip within 2 s if the applied current is half its rating.

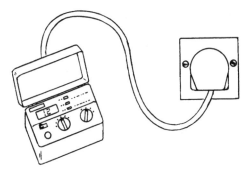

Fig. 4.6   RCD tester connected to a socket outlet for a test.

Where an RCD is deliberately time delayed to provide discrimination with another, the rated tripping current should cause the device to operate at between half and full rated tripping time, both plus 200 ms. For example, if a 100 mA RCD with a rated tripping time of 300 ms is tested, an applied current of 100 mA should cause it to trip anywhere between the limits of:

$$\frac{300}{2} + 200 = 150 + 200 = 350 \text{ ms}$$

and $300 + 200 = 500 \text{ ms}$

The RCD tester is an electronic device which requires current from the supply for its operation. This current is usually a few milliamperes and returns through the neutral, so that it has no effect on the test of a single-phase supply. When an RCD connected to a three-phase three-wire supply (which has no neutral) is being tested, the tester must be connected to the neutral of another circuit to obtain the necessary supply.

4.8   Testing with Infra-Red Cameras

These devices will give a remote reading of temperature, and are used to investigate possible hot spots in cables or in equipment whilst they are in use. It is a particularly useful method for discovering loose connections, which may be on the point of failure. The major advantage is that equipment temperature can be monitored without disconnection of the supply.

4.9   Test Instrument Requirements

Guidance Note 3 makes it clear that all instruments used for measurement of an electrical installation must have accuracy no lower than that quoted later in this section. This accuracy must be verified by regular calibration, which in practice will mean sending the instrument to a laboratory or test house where its performance can be compared with that of a standard. The Note gives no indication of what is meant by 'regular calibration'. It would seem that for instruments used only occasionally this could be every two years, but that annual recalibration should be the norm for regularly used testers.

The Safety-in-Use Standard is BS EN 61010, 'Safety Requirements for Electrical Equipment for Measurement, Control and Laboratory Use'. The performance Standard, which also requires compliance with the above standard, is BS EN 61557. This Standard is published in eight parts that together cover all the types of instruments used to test electrical installations. Test leads, including prods and clips, must be in good order and have no cracked or broken insulation. Fused test leads should be used to reduce the risk of arcing under fault conditions.

The accuracy required for electronic instruments is generally ±5%, whilst for analogue instruments the accuracy at full-scale deflection should be ±2%, which will give the ±5% norm over the useful part of their scales. The detailed requirements for the various types of instrument in use are as follows.

Low resistance ohmmeter BS EN 61557-4

Basic instrument accuracy required is ±5%
Test voltage, a.c or d.c., between 4 V and 24 V
Test current not less than 200 mA
Able to measure within 0.01 Ω (resolution of 0.01)

Insulation resistance testing instrument BS EN 61557-2

Test voltage variable (see Table 4.1)
Minimum current at lowest insulation resistance 1 mA
Basic instrument accuracy required is ±5%
Must be able to discharge 5 μF, which has become charged during test

Earth-fault loop impedance testing instrument BS EN 61557-3

Must provide 20 to 25 A for two cycles or for four half-cycles
Basic instrument accuracy required is ±5%
Able to measure within 0.01 Ω (resolution of 0.01)

Residual current device (RCD) testing instrument

Must perform the required range of tests (see Section 4.7)
Suitable for standard RCD ratings of 6, 10, 30 100, 300 and 500 mA
Must NOT apply test current for more than 2 s
Current applied must be accurate to ± 10%
Able to measure opening time to within 1 ms (resolution of 1)
Must measure opening time with an accuracy of ±5%.

Earth electrode resistance testing instrument BS EN 61557-5

Basic instrument accuracy required is ±5%
Able to measure within 0.01 Ω (resolution of 0.01).

The **accuracy** declared for an instrument relates to the full-scale deflection for an analogue instrument or to the highest reading on the scale in use for a digital type. The best accuracy will thus be obtained by using the lowest possible range on any type of instrument. Instrument errors are not constant and will vary as the measured level changes. Other factors, too, can affect accuracy, such as battery condition, ambient temperature, operator competence, and the operating orientation of the instrument. Accuracy will also depend on field errors, which are due to factors such as stray magnetic fields, thermocouple effects, mains voltage variation, lead resistance, contact resistance, mains pickup and so on.

The **resolution** of an instrument is its ability to display a reading to the required degree of accuracy. For example, the measured earth-fault loop impedance of a socket outlet circuit protected by a 30 A miniature circuit breaker type 2 should not exceed 1.14 Ω. If our measuring instrument is a three-digit type with a lowest range of 99.9 Ω we could obtain readings of 1.1 Ω or of 1.2 Ω, but not of 1.14 Ω, because the resolution is not close enough, the best value being 0.1 Ω. If the instrument has a 9.99 Ω range, it could read 1.14 Ω since its resolution is 0.01 Ω.

4.10   The Installation Operational Manual

When we take delivery of a new car, we expect to be given a handbook giving the technical and operating details of the vehicle. In exactly the same way, a new electrical installation, no matter how insignificant it may be, must have an installation operational manual. This is unlikely to be in the form of a printed book, but is more likely to be a folder containing all the data concerning the installation. Items to be included are:

1 Full design details including calculations such as those for cable sizes
2 A complete schematic diagram of the installation showing switch and control gear details, cable sizes and so on
3 A set of 'as fitted' drawings showing the complete installation
4 A copy of the original electrical installation certificate showing all test results
5 Copies of all periodic inspection and test certificates
6 Copies of any minor works certificates detailing amendments to the installation.

The completed manual should be retained by the user of the installation, who, in some cases, will be the maintenance manager. It is important that the manual is kept up to date.

Chapter 5

Industrial Control Gear and Transformers

5.1 The Need for Records

It is essential for every industrial maintenance manager to have a register of all the industrial switchgear and all transformers on site. This should include the manufacturer, the model, the type, and the history in terms of both maintenance and modification. The maximum prospective fault current for every item of switchgear must be ascertained, so that with knowledge of the load to be switched it can be decided if the equipment is fit for the intended operation.

Maximum prospective fault current is the highest value of fault current that can possibly arise at the location concerned. It can be calculated by dividing the system voltage by the minimum impedance of the system under fault conditions. But how do we arrive at a value for this impedance? It will usually be the impedance value of the fault loop, typically the impedance of the phase and neutral conductors from the supply transformer. In the case of an earth fault, the neutral impedance would need to be replaced by that of the return earth path. If, as is often the case, the fault applies to all three-phases, the neutral or earth path would not apply, and the maximum prospective fault current would be at least twice that of a similar single-phase system.

The foregoing suggests that accurate determination of the maximum prospective fault current will be difficult. So how is it done? There are three methods.

1 Calculate or measure the impedance of the path followed by the fault current, assuming a zero-impedance fault at the point which will result in the lowest impedance value and hence the highest calculated fault current. The value chosen must always be the highest which may be possible

2 Measure the value. Instruments are available for this purpose, usually based on earth-fault loop impedance instruments, but taking

the phase to neutral loop rather than phase to earth. The problem will be that such instruments are intended for use on the smaller installation, and will seldom read above 20 kA. Specialist devices are available for measurement of higher values.

3   Ask the Supply Company for the prospective fault current level at the origin of the installation and modify it in the light of the imped-ance of the fault path from the origin to the required point. The problem with this method is that most Supply Companies quote very high fault levels. There is also the danger that subsequent changes to the layout or the capacity of the supply system could increase the value.

None of the methods is easy or fool proof. From a pure engineering stand-point it would be best to assume a very high value of prospective fault current. But this is likely to prove costly, since the higher the breaking capacity of a device, the more expensive it will be. The subject of prospec-tive fault current has been considered in Section 4.5, Table 4.2 showing suggested values for typical types, sizes and lengths of supply cables.

5.2   Oil-Filled Switchgear

The inert gas sulphur hexafluoride (SF_6) is in wide use as an insulator in high voltage switchgear. There has been a major change in the philosophy as far as oil filling is concerned. It is now considered to be a possible source of danger due to the (remote) possibility of an explosion of burning oil. This is the principal reason for the increasing use of air-break and SF_6 equipments. Exploding oil equipment would not only present a fire risk, but would also be very dangerous to workers in the vicinity. It must be stressed that properly maintained and operated oil-filled switchgear is perfectly safe.

Where such switchgear is in use, particularly if it was manufactured before 1970, those responsible should obtain a copy of Health and Safety Executive document 483/27. This gives details of the risks concerned as well as information that should control or eliminate them.

Where such switchgear is present, all the information needed for completion of Table 5.1 should be available, as well as:

1   The voltage rating
2   The type of operating mechanism
3   Date last serviced or maintained

Table 5.1 Switchgear Data	
Substation identification Location Switch number Make Year manufactured Year commissioned Serial number Year modified Type Duty Serial number Load rating A Fault rating MVA	Full data to be filled in as required

4 Details of modifications or repairs
5 Type of electrical protection with details of the settings
6 Type of operating mechanism (manual, power or stored energy)
7 Details of fitted arc control devices

Maintenance staff who work on oil-filled switchgear should be skilled and experienced in all aspects of the work, and must be provided with full information concerning the history of the equipment in terms of modifications, faults and failures.

5.3   Oil-Filled Transformers

The hazards associated with oil-filled circuit breakers were explored in the previous section. The same problems apply to oil-filled transformers, so that oil-filled types are becoming less common, although there are still very large numbers in use. In an attempt to reduce the risks associated with oil as a cooling medium, poly-chlorinated benzines (PCBs) were used for a time. This material was found to be carcinogenic (it causes cancer) and any equipments found to contain this material should be removed from service and treated with the greatest care after seeking expert advice.

The register of data concerning each transformer (see Table 5.2) should be carefully completed and made available to maintenance staff.

As with switchgear, staff required to work on transformers must be provided with full information on the history of the equipment with which they are dealing.

Table 5.2 Transformer Data

Substation identification Location Transformer number Make Year manufactured Year commissioned Serial number Rating Vector group Primary/secondary voltage Tap range Tap steps Percentage impedance Oil capacity Breather Conservator Weight	Full data to be filled in as required

5.4 Routine Maintenance

High voltage switchgear and transformers require regular and expert routine maintenance. This work can be considered to consist of three activities, inspection, examination and overhaul. Table 5.3 indicates the maximum recommended intervals between each activity.

Table 5.3 Suggested Maintenance intervals for 11 kV equipment

Maintenance activity	Maximum periods between maintenance activities
Inspection	1 year
Examination	5 years
Overhaul	15 years

It is important to appreciate that the intervals given in Table 5.3 are the absolute maximum periods. Where operating conditions are particularly difficult or where switchgear is operated frequently, they should be reduced. Oil circuit breakers should be overhauled after every operation following a fault, and SF_6 circuit breakers need to be examined as soon as possible after a fault operation.

Maintenance schedules follow in Tables 5.4, 5.5, 5.6 and 5.7 for various types of switchgear and for transformers. Where the item is marked X the required action must be taken. Reports and certificates must support all these activities after completion.

Table 5.4 Maintenance Schedule for Oil Circuit Breakers

Maintenance operation	Inspection	Examination	Overhaul
General inspection	X	X	X
Protective relays settings check	X	X	X
Time limit fuses inspection	X	X	X
Cleaning		X	X
Closing and trip mechanism		X	X
Main and arcing contacts		X	X
Shutters	X	X	X
Bushings		X	X
Winding and truck mechanisms		X	X
Interlocks	X	X	X
Auxiliary contacts		X	X
Secondary wiring and fuses		X	X
Insulation test		X	X
Earth connections		X	X
Insulating oil		X	X
Heaters		X	X
Devices for arc control		X	X
Tank and tank linings			X
Switchgear spouts			X
Venting and gas seals			X
Current and voltage transformers			X
Operational check	X	X	X

Table 5.5 Maintenance Schedule for Oil Switches

Maintenance operation	Inspection	Examination	Overhaul
General inspection	X	X	X
Cleaning*		X	X
Withdrawal locking system*	X	X	X
Insulators and bushings*			X
Safety shutters*	X	X	X
Insulating oil		X	X
Main arcing contacts			X
Arc control devices			X
Operating mechanism			X
Isolating contacts*			X
Switchgear spouts			X
High voltage fuse connections			X
Tank and tank linings	X		X
Interlocks			X
Auxiliary contacts			X
Weather shields			X
Earth connections			X
Insulation test			X
Operational check*		X	X

* applies to withdrawable types only

Table 5.6   Maintenance Schedule for SF$_6$ Switchgear

Maintenance operation	Inspection	Examination	Overhaul
General inspection	X	X	X
Cleaning*		X	X
Leak tests		X	X
Lubrication		X	X
Operational check	X	X	X

* applies to withdrawable types only

Table 5.7   Maintenance Schedule for Oil Filled Transformers

Maintenance operation	Inspection	Examination	Overhaul
General exterior inspection	X	X	X
Breather	X	X	X
Oil level	X	X	X
Suspect oil sample and test	X		
Oil sample and test		X	X
Check external connections and conductors			X
Main tank			X
Clean and inspect conservator			X
Clean exterior			X
LV and HV connections check			X
Visual inspection of transformer core			X

Chapter 6

Alarm and Fire Detection Systems

6.1 Types of Alarm System

The design, installation and maintenance of fire detection and alarm systems are covered by BS 5839: 1988 'Fire Detection and Alarm Systems for Buildings'.

Fire detection and alarm systems are divided into eight categories by the BS. These categories are:

Type P   Automatic detection and alarm systems for the protection of property only

Type P1   Detection and alarm systems installed throughout the protected buildings

Type P2   Detection and alarm systems installed only in defined parts of the buildings

Type L   Automatic detection and alarm for the protection of life

Type L1   Detection and alarm systems installed throughout the protected buildings

Type L2   Detection and alarm systems installed only in defined parts of the buildings

NOTE that a Type L2 system should also include the coverage required for a Type L3 system (see below).

Type L3   Detection and alarm systems installed only for the protection of escape routes

Type M   Manual alarm system. There is no sub-division

BS 5839 uses the letter 'D' to designate systems installed in dwellings. Thus an automatic system for the protection of life and installed in a block of flats will be shown as Type LD2.

It is important that the escape procedures to be followed on operation of the alarm are known before an alarm system is designed. Such design must take account of how the evacuation will be conducted, including the possible need for a secure public address system to give advice. It must be noted that a Type L3 system is installed only for warning on an escape route, the system itself is not expected to protect people who are fighting the fire.

6.2   Power supplies and cables

Each fire detection and alarm system must be connected to the mains supply by its own isolator, which must be coloured RED and must be labelled:

> **FIRE ALARM: DO NOT SWITCH OFF**

To prevent unwanted operation, the isolator may be contained in an enclosure with a breakable glass cover. If the isolator is fed from the live side of a supply so that the main switch does not switch it off, there should be a second label, which reads:

> **Warning: This supply remains live when the main switch is turned off**

In addition the main switch must carry the label:

> **Warning: The fire alarm supply remains live when this switch is turned off**

Alternatively, if the main switch directly controls the fire alarm system, it should carry the following label:

> **Warning: This switch also controls the supply to the fire alarm system**

The operation of a fire alarm system is entirely dependent on the integrity of the cables connecting its various components, such as alarm sounders, supply system, bells, sirens and so on. An important part of the maintenance is thus to ensure, as far as possible, that the cables will remain in working condition should a fire occur. It follows that the alarms should continue to sound during a fire, even if the supplies to detectors or other points of initiation have been destroyed. This means that the cabling used for the alarms should be able to continue to operate for at least half an hour in the event of fire.

The cables used should therefore be either:

1 mineral insulated copper sheathed cables to BS 6207, or
2 cables complying with BS 6387 and meeting category requirements AWX or SWX.

Other types of cable may be used provided that they are protected from the fire by being buried under at least 12 mm of plaster, or are separated from the fire risk by a wall, partition or floor having a resistance to fire of at least half an hour.

As well as having good fire performance as indicated above, it is sensible to segregate alarm cables from others so that they will not be damaged in the event of faults on the other circuits. Generally speaking, fire alarm circuits should be separated from all other electrical wiring by one of the following methods.

1 Using a dedicated conduit, trunking, ducting or channel system for fire alarm cables
2 Separating alarm cables from others using non-combustible partitions which are rigid and continuous
3 Using mineral insulated copper cables having an insulating sheath
4 Using cables complying with BS 7269 which have a metallic and insulating sheaths
5 Ensuring that there is a space of at least 300 mm from other cables.

The wiring of an alarm system is required to have the same regular inspection and testing as other fixed installations. Intervals not exceeding five years are specified for periodic test and inspection.

6.3 Record Keeping

Drawings and operating instructions for the alarm system must be maintained and should ideally be kept close to the control and indicator equipment.

One person should be ultimately responsible for the system, and should maintain a log book which includes:

1 His own name, location and telephone extension number
2 Full details of the servicing arrangements

3   A complete record of all alarms including the location of initiation. The list must include practice, false, test and genuine alarms

4   The dates, times and nature of every defect or fault

5   Full data , including dates and times, of when these defects or faults were rectified

6   The date and time of each service of the system

7   The dates and types of all system tests

8   The dates and types of all system services

9   The dates and times when the system was disconnected or non-operational

10   Full details of alterations to the system, including dates

11   Full details of the people and/or organisations carrying out work of any kind on the system.

The layout of a typical log book is shown opposite.

The responsible person must have the authority to ensure that:

1   The detection and alarm system is properly serviced and maintained

2   All staff are instructed and trained in the actions they should take in the event of an alarm

3   The local Fire Authority approves of the escape plan

4   All escape routes and access to fire alarm and extinguishing equipment are kept clear at all times

6.4   False Alarms

False alarms will not only waste valuable time, but may also result in a loss of confidence in the system, which could have serious results. Notices should be widely displayed to draw attention to the system. It is particularly important to ensure that automatic alarm dialling systems to the Fire Service (999 or 112) are disconnected before a routine test. Staff, both those working on the site and those visiting it, should be made aware of the alarm system and of the precautions to be taken if false alarms are to be avoided. Where engineering or building work is undertaken on the site, those concerned must be given advice so that they take precautions to avoid damage, disconnection, or false operation of the alarm system.

A responsible executive should maintain this book, making sure that every event is properly recorded.

Events will include:
1 Real alarms
2 False alarms
3 Pre-alarm warnings
4 Tests
5 Faults
6 Temporary disconnection
7 Visits by installing or servicing engineers, with data concerning the work
   performed on each visit

Responsible person ....

Address ....

....

Telephone number and extension of responsible person ....

System installed by ....

Maintained by ....

Date of cessation of maintenance contract ....

Telephone number of servicing contractor ....

Date	Time	Event	Action required	Date Completed	Initials

6.5   Servicing

Servicing is likely to be best arranged on a regular basis. All defects that come to light must be entered in the logbook. Details of the checks and work required at each regular service follow.

Daily service
  1 The alarm panel indicates normal operation – if there is a fault,
     check that this has been recorded

2 Unless there is continuous monitoring, test the automatic link to the fire brigade

3 Confirm that faults recorded yesterday have been rectified

Weekly service

1 At least one alarm initiator (break glass point, automatic sensor, etc) on one zone must be tested to verify the ability of the system to receive the signal and to sound the alarm

2 Visually inspect the batteries and their connections where possible. Report and rectify defects

3 Where prime movers (petrol or diesel engines) are involved, check fuel, lubrication and coolant

4 If the system has no more than thirteen zones, at least one zone must be tested each week. Where there are more than thirteen zones, more than one zone must be tested every week to ensure that each is tested at least every thirteen weeks

5 Enter any defects detected in the log book

Monthly service

1 Where automatically started standby generators are used, they must be operated by a simulated failure of the main power supply system and allowed to run for one hour. Checks should be carried out to ensure that the operation of the generator(s) has not affected them

2 After testing, fuel, lubrication and coolant levels must be checked and adjusted.

Three-monthly service

1 Confirm that all faults shown in the log book have been rectified

2 When a detector in each zone is operated, check that the alarms and indicators work correctly

3 All ancillary functions of the control panel must be tested

4 Simulation of appropriate faults is used to check all fault indicators

5 All batteries are examined and checked, with necessary measurement of voltage and, where appropriate, of specific gravity of the electrolyte

6 A complete visual inspection of the building should be carried out to ensure that no changes in structure or in use have taken place which require alteration to the alarm system layout

Annual service

1 All cables and fittings must be visually inspected to ensure that they are secure
2 All equipment must be checked and examined for signs of ageing, of wear or other indication of possible malfunction
3 Every detector must be checked for correct operation

6.6 Certification

A new detection and alarm system should be certified on completion of inspection and testing with a certificate such as the following:

Fire Alarm System Certificate of Installation and Commissioning

For the user

Area protected ....

Occupier ....

Address ....

....

I confirm that I have been made aware of BS 5839 and in particular to clauses 14 (false alarms), 28 and 29 (user responsibilities)

Signed .... Status .... Date ....

For and on behalf of the user ....

For the installer

The installation has been inspected and tested to BS 5839 standards for insulation resistance of all conductors, and earthing. The operation of the entire system has been tested and it is certified that it complies with all the requirements of BS 5839 other than the following deviations.

....

Signed (Commissioning engineer) ....

Name in block capitals ....

For and on behalf of (installer) ....

The system log book is situated ....

The system documentation is situated ....

Area protected ....

Occupier ....

Address ....

....

I confirm that I have been made aware of BS 5839 and in particular to clauses 14 (false alarms), 28 and 29 (user responsibilities)

Signed .... Status .... Date ....

For and on behalf of the user ....

For periodic testing of a fire alarm system, the following certificate is appropriate

---

Certificate for Testing a Fire Alarm System

This certificate relates to the testing of the fire alarm system at

Protected area ....

Name of occupier ....

Address ....

....
The system has been inspected and tested to the requirements of BS 5839.

Work carried out and covered by this Certificate is as follows. (Items not covered are deleted).

      Alterations and extensions to the existing system
      Quarterly inspection and test
      Annual inspection and test
      Servicing following a fault
      Servicing following a pre-alarm warning
      Servicing following a false alarm
      Service following a fire
      Other non-routine service (specify)

....

....

Signed .... Status .... Date ....

Name in block letters ....

For ....

Chapter 7

Emergency Lighting

7.1 General

Perhaps the prime purpose of emergency lighting is to allow the occupants of a building to escape from it in the event of the loss of the primary lighting system. This may well be as the result of a fire or other event which could quickly become a disaster if escape is hindered in any way.

Another very important function of emergency lighting is to allow staff in switch and control rooms to continue their work in the event of the failure of the main lighting system. This may be to restore supplies or to allow dangerous plant to be shut down.

7.1 Safety signs

The European Council directive 1992/58EEC is implemented by the Health and Safety (Safety Signs and Signals) Regulations 1996 in specifying the minimum requirements for safety signs in the workplace. It lays down the requirements for emergency escape and fire safety signs. These signs should be clear in all circumstances, and with this in mind they are required to be mounted at between 2 m and 2.5 m above floor level.

Escape route, exit and emergency exit signs must be illuminated so that they are always legible. In the event of a failure of the main lighting system, they are required to remain illuminated by the emergency lighting system. This illumination may be from

    a) an internally-illuminated sign, which should comply with BS 5499 Part 1, or

    b) an external emergency lighting luminaire

7.2.1 Sign Colours

The colours of signs must comply with the requirements of 58EEC, which are shown in Table 7.1.

Table 7.1	Colours required for safety signs	
Colour	*Purpose*	*Information or instruction*
Red	Prohibition sign	Dangerous behaviour
Red	Fire fighting equipment	Identification of location
Red	Danger alarm	Stop, shutdown & emergency cut-out devices
Green	Emergency escape and first aid signs	Doors, exit routes & equipment facilities

7.2.2 *Signs*

See inside back cover

For information on the siting and size of these signs see Section 16.3.

7.3   Escape Luminaire Siting

An emergency luminaire must be placed in every position where it will help persons to escape or where it will facilitate operation of the alarm system. The following positions are a requirement of BS 5266.

1   All exit doors
2   Changes in direction of the escape route
3   The intersection of corridors
4   At changes of floor level
5   Staircases
6   Close to every fire alarm call point
7   Near fire fighting equipment
8   At all safety signs, including exit signs
9   Outside final exits

The same British Standard also recommends that emergency luminaires should be provided in the following locations.

10   Moving stairs and walkways
11   Lift cars
12   Outside all exits
13   Toilets and similar situations which exceed 8 m² in area

7.4   Installation of Emergency Lighting

Two basic types are in use for emergency lighting.
1 Self-contained types, which take their supply from the mains when it is available but switch to internal batteries on mains failure
2 Central battery type, where a central supply from batteries feeds them.

7.4.1 Wiring

Wiring to self-contained luminaires is not considered to be part of the emergency lighting circuit, since its integrity does not affect the operation of the luminaire in the event of mains failure. All other wiring to emergency luminaires must be protected from physical damage and from fire. All such cables must be routed through areas of low fire risk. Wiring should either be in mineral insulated cables to BS 6207, or cables that comply with category B of BS 6387. Such cables are either those with thermosetting insulation to BS 7629 or armoured types to BS 7846. Other cables, such as PVC insulated types in steel or rigid PVC conduits are permissible, provided that they are protected from fire. Such protection must be by burying the cable in the structure of the building, or running them in situations of minimal fire risk and where a fire-resistant wall, floor or partition protects them.

7.4.2 Supplies

It is important to appreciate that where the supply is switched off at night, this may, unless special arrangements are made, prevent the charging of a central battery or of those in self-contained luminaires. It will be appreciated that when the central supply is switched off, the emergency lighting will see this as a mains failure and come into operation, discharging its batteries in the process.

7.4.3 Isolation

Special precautions to be taken to avoid unexpected switching of the supply to an alarm system are covered in Section 6.2 of this book. Although written specifically for alarms, they apply equally to emergency lighting. Where necessary the required label should read:

> **Emergency/Escape/Standby Lighting**
> **Do NOT switch off**

Supplies for safety services are the subject of Chapter 56 of BS 7671: 1992 'Requirements for Electrical Installations'.

7.5   Maintenance of Emergency Lighting

When an emergency lighting system is completed, the installer will provide a completion certificate. Maintenance of the system should be carried out on a daily, monthly, six-monthly and three-yearly basis as described below. All these maintenance activities must be recorded in a logbook (similar to, but separate from, that described for a fire alarm system in Chapter 6). The logbook must record all of the following information.

1   The date of the completion certificate, and of certificates for extensions and alterations
2   Dates and details of every service, inspection and test of the system
3   Dates and details of all reported defects, together with details of remedial action taken
4   Dates and details of all alterations to the emergency lighting system

Details of the actions required at each of the periodic maintenance events are as follows.

7.5.1 Daily service

a) Check that faults already entered in the logbook have been rectified
b) Check that lamps in all maintained luminaires are lit
c) Record any faults found in the logbook
d) Check that the main control panel of central batteries or engine-driven plant shows a healthy indication

7.5.2 Monthly service

Some of the tests involve a simulated failure of the mains supply. The period of simulated failure must not exceed 25% of the rated duration of the standby batteries to ensure that they are not depleted. Where the required checks cannot be made in this time, the process must be repeated after the batteries have been fully recharged.

a) Simulate a failure of the main supply for long enough to check that all self-contained and illuminated exit signs are operating.
b) A similar simulation must be carried out to check the correct operation of a central battery system.
c) This simulation must be applied to test engine-driven generating plants, which must energise the emergency lighting for at least one hour.
d) Fuel levels, as well as oil and coolant supplies on engine-driven generating plant, must be checked and adjusted.

e) For engine-driven back-up plant with automatic starting using batteries, simulated mains failure must be carried out with the engine prevented from starting. After this check, normal starting must be allowed on simulated mains failure, with the generating plant energising the emergency lighting for at least an hour.

7.5.3 Six-monthly service

The full monthly tests should be carried out, plus operation of three-hour rated luminaires, signs and back-up batteries for one hour. Where these devices have a rated duration of one hour, the test should be for fifteen minutes. No mention is made of two-hour systems, but common sense would suggest that they should be tested for thirty minutes. The control panels must be checked for healthy indications.

7.5.4 Three-yearly service

The full monthly inspection should be carried out. In addition, every self-contained luminaire, internally-illuminated sign, central battery system and generator back-up battery must be tested for its full duration. The complete installation must also be examined to confirm that it still complies with its stated form.

Additionally, it is required that self-contained luminaires with sealed batteries that are more than three years old should be subjected to the three-year test every year to ensure that they have adequate storage capacity.

7.6   Duration of luminaire output

There are two types of emergency lighting luminaire.

7.6.1 Maintained emergency lighting – given the designation M.
This is a system where all emergency lighting is in operation at all times.

7.6.2 Non-maintained emergency lighting – given the designation NM.
This system is one in which emergency lighting is only operational when normal lighting fails.

The number of hours for which both types can maintain their light output to an acceptable level after the supply failure is added to the designation. For example, designation NM/2 indicates a non-maintained luminaire with duration of two hours. Evacuation is unlikely to take longer than one hour, but Local Authority licences sometimes require extended periods.

The minimum requirements for duration are shown in Table 7.2.

Table 7.2   Emergency Lighting Duration Requirements

Type of Premises			Minimum Category
Residential	With sleeping accommodation, such as hotels, nursing homes, guest houses, hospitals, educational establishments with boarders	10 bedrooms or more	NM/3 or M/3
		Small – less than 10 bedrooms and with not more than one floor above or below ground level	NM/2 or M/2
Non-residential	Care or treatment, such as clinics, special schools, and so on.		NM/1
Non-residential	Recreational, such as public houses, restaurants, concert halls, sports halls, exhibition halls, theatres, and so on.	Buildings where lighting can be dimmed or for the consumption of alcohol	NM/2
		Other	NM/2 or M/2
		Where not more than 250 people are present	NM/1 or M/1
Non-residential	Recreational such as cinemas, ten pin bowling venues, bingo halls, dance halls, ballrooms, and so on.		As non-residential immediately above, but subject to BS CP 1007 for cinemas
Non-residential	Laboratories, colleges and schools		NM/1 or M/1
Non-residential	Industrial, such as manufacturing, storage, etc.		NM/1 or M/1
Non-residential	Museums, art galleries, shops, offices, libraries, town halls.	Where lighting may be dimmed	M/1
		Other	M/1 or NM/1

NOTE that, as stated above,   M indicates a maintained luminaire
NM indicates a non-maintained luminaire
The digit after '/' indicates the period (hours) of illumination after mains failure.

Chapter 8
Data Processing Systems

8.1   Introduction

This Chapter concerns the increasing number of installations (often called 'data cable networks') devoted to the transmission and processing of data. Increasingly, such transmission systems are making use of optic fibres, as opposed to normal metallic conductors, to carry the data which, in the vast majority of cases, will be in digital, rather than analogue, form. This means that the cabling system will be carrying pulses, rather than electric currents whose waveforms are important. The rate at which these pulses are transmitted is increasing at an alarming rate, sometimes being in the GB/s range (giga-bits per second – one gigabit is equal to one thousand million pulses).

The business of data cabling is a complex one; even the language used, based as it is on American practice, is foreign to most UK electricians. This is a very specialist field, for which the correct knowledge and experience are essential. Maintenance of data cabling systems requires the use of specialist testers and techniques, and is often driven by the implementation of specialist computer software, which may well be written exclusively for one particular installation.

British Standards are somewhat limited in this respect, being confined to BS 6266: 1992 which is concerned with the fire protection of data cabling systems.

8.2   Cable Management Systems

Cable management systems (CMS) are usually in the form of computer software, but sometimes are simply paperwork in a ring binder. The CMS will detail precisely the cable network as presently installed, and is often considered as an essential requirement for the maintenance and extension or alteration of a network. Knowing exactly, and with certainty, what is installed and where it is located, is essential when working on a system.

There are many important reasons for having an effective cable management system. Some of them are:

1 To identify which equipment is being used, which is out of use and which is on standby

2 To determine which cables, conductors and fibres are free or in use, and what purposes are assigned to them

3 To maintain an identification system so that a disaster recovery plan can be implemented if required

4 To maintain complete records of faults, alterations and other events

5 To reduce labour time and costs in tracing undocumented circuits

6 To facilitate the transfer of users from one cabling system to another when the need arises

7 To document and maintain circuit and cable test data

8.3   The Electrical Installation

BS 6266 covers cable, emergency switches and electrical installations. It thus confines itself to the electrical supply system, rather than addressing the data-cabling network.

8.3.1 Cables

It is essential that all wiring should comply with BS 7671 and that all cables should be protected from the effects of fire. Where run in floor and ceiling voids, power cables (unless mineral insulated or steel wire armoured types) must be installed in metal conduit or in metal trunking. Data cables should be similarly protected unless clipped to a metal tray. The emission of smoke and corrosive fumes when cable insulation burns is an on-going problem. Only low smoke-emitting cables to BS 7622 should be used. Those suitable are:

1 Mineral insulated cables (BS 6207)

2 Armoured cables with thermosetting insulation (BS 6724)

3 Non-armoured cables with thermosetting insulation (BS 7211)

4 Thermosetting insulated cables (BS 7629)

5 600/1000 V armoured fire resistant cables (BS 7846)

8.3.2 Emergency switches

It is important that the electrical supplies to electronic data processing equipment, air conditioning and all main power supplies, except lighting and smoke extraction, can be switched off quickly in the event of an emergency. Properly labelled emergency switches should thus be placed near exit doors or at other suitable positions.

A main isolator controlling all power supplies to the electronic data processing area, with the exceptions of lighting and smoke extraction, must be provided at the main entrance to the area and marked:

> ## FIRE EMERGENCY SWITCH

8.3.3 *Electrical installations*

The recommendations are:
1 No electrical equipment other than cables, junction boxes and smoke detectors should be installed in floor voids.
2 Power cables should have no joints.
3 Power cables must be routed round the perimeter of the data processing room to reduce radiation interference.
4 The number of junction boxes situated under floors should be kept to a minimum.
5 Such junction boxes should be fully enclosed and must be metal clad.

8.4   Display Screen Regulations

Basic to the use of data management systems is the use of display screens. For a number of years these devices have been cathode ray tubes, although increasingly flat liquid crystal display types are appearing. The Health and Safety (Display Screen Equipment) Regulations require a risk assessment to be carried out for each visual display unit workstation. The Health and Safety Executive in their publication L26, Display Screen Equipment at Work, provide a guide to the regulations. The assessment required is not usually the prerogative of the maintenance manger, but it is strongly advised that the manager include the publication amongst his reference data.

It is likely that at least one display screen station will be included in the office of the maintenance manager, so he needs to be aware of the requirements. He should be able to:
1 Assess the risk of using the workstation
2 Record his assessment and see that it brought to the attention of the responsible person if action is needed

3 Realise that he is unlikely to be an expert in this field, and to seek help as necessary

The assessment will need to be reviewed in the event of changes in the environment, such as alterations to natural or artificial lighting. Reassessment will also be required if changes are made to furniture, such as the height of the display or of the operator seating.

Chapter 9

Appliances and Equipment

9.1 The Need for Inspection and Testing

9.1.1 *The Law*

The Electricity at Work Regulations were made as part of the Health and Safety at Work Act etc. requirements. They became law in Great Britain in 1990 and in Northern Ireland in 1992. Many electrical accidents are concerned with the use (and the misuse) of portable appliances, so the regular testing and inspection regime which has now become standard is of obvious importance.

9.1.2 *Portable Appliances*

The term 'portable appliance' is somewhat misleading. The equipment concerned may be portable, hand-held, movable, stationary, built-in or fixed, but must still be inspected and tested to comply with the Act.

Some explanation of terms used for equipment is therefore necessary.

Portable appliance weighs less than 18 kg and is intended to be moved whilst in operation. Examples are the food mixer, fan heater, vacuum cleaner, toaster, etc.

Movable equipment (sometimes called transportable) either weighs less than 18 kg and is not fixed (such as an electric fire) or has wheels or castors so that it can be moved as necessary (such as an air conditioning unit).

Hand-held appliance or equipment is portable and held during use (such as electric drill, electric screwdriver, hair dryer, etc.).

Stationary equipment or appliance has a weight of more than 18 kg and is not provided with a carrying handle (such as refrigerator or washing machine).

Fixed equipment or appliance is secured in position (such as a towel rail or bathroom heater).

Information technology equipment is general office equipment such as computers, plotters, scanners, printers and photocopiers. Special care in selection of testing voltage is needed when testing such devices (particularly insulation resistance testing) since many of the components used are dangerously susceptible to high voltages.

9.1.3 Register of Equipment

Clearly it is important that the responsible person in an organisation knows what items of equipment are available and which thus need testing. Every item must have clear identification so that there can be no doubt that it is the particular item that is to be, or has been, tested. This will usually take the form of a descriptive label that will carry the name of the item, together with its serial number. If a PAT (portable appliance tester) is in use, the label may take the form of a bar code. This has the advantage of immediate identification by the bar code reader, but has the disadvantage that the normal person will be unable to decipher it. In these cases both methods should be used.

An equipment register must be made and maintained in correct order. Any new items of equipment must be added, and those scrapped clearly marked as such in the register. The form of a typical register is shown in Table 9.1.

Table 9.1 Typical inspection and testing register of equipment

Register number	Location	Equipment description	Serial number	Frequency of inspection and test	
				Formal visual inspection	Combined inspection and testing

9.2 Types of Test

All types of electrical equipments are subject to a series of tests. These are:

1 Type approval testing is required during manufacture or production to ensure compliance with the relevant British Standards.
2 Routine testing by the manufacturer on completion and before putting into service.
3 Tests carried out after repair to ensure correct and safe operation.
4 Inspection and testing during service life.

This Chapter of this Guide deals with the last item only.

9.3 Types of Equipment

Electrical equipment has a number of forms of construction, the most usual being detailed as follows.

9.3.1 Class 0 Equipment

This type is of historic interest only, covering equipment with exposed metal parts but with only a two-core feed and thus without earth. The very old brass table lamp with twin twisted flex to feed it is a typical example, which, hopefully, only exists in our memories. Class 01 is similar, covering the same type of equipment but having an earth terminal which is not connected because there is only a two-core cord.

9.3.2 Class I Equipment

Equipment of this type has the normal insulation to protect the user, but also has a protective conductor (earth wire). In the event of insulation failure a fault current will flow to earth, operating the protective device and thus protecting the user. Since the safety of this class of equipment is reliant on the integrity of the earthing system, more frequent testing and inspection is required than for Class II equipment.

9.3.3 Class II Equipment   indicated by the symbol ▫

Equipments of this class have the normal insulation as do those of Class I, but also have a second layer of insulation. They are sometimes referred to as "double insulated". Thus there is no need to earth metal parts, and Class II equipment is usually fed through two-core flexible cords. An exception to this is certain information technology apparatus that requires an earth connection for the correct operation of its filter circuits.

9.3.4 Class III Equipment

This type of equipment is unusual and provides protection from electric shock by being fed from an extra-low voltage source (separated extra-low voltage or SELV) such as an isolating transformer to BS 3535.

The equipment should be marked with the symbol ⟨111⟩

and the transformer with the symbol

9.4   Frequency of Inspections and Tests

The Electricity at Work Regulations do not include requirements for the elapsed period between inspections and tests. They simply require that the equipment must be maintained 'so as to prevent danger'; it is for the user to decide on the frequency, but he should always bear in mind that in the event of an accident his decisions will be scrutinised. Three factors will need to be considered in making the decision. They are

1 The care likely to be exercised by the equipment user, and the likelihood of damage to the appliance being reported by him.

2 The environment in which the equipment is used. For example, appliances used in an office are less likely to suffer damage than those on a construction site.

3 The construction of the equipment – suitability of purpose and robustness will affect the possible frequency of attention.

Table 9.2 overleaf indicates suggested frequencies of inspection and testing for a variety of equipments in a number of situations. The following abbreviations are used in the second column of the Table.

H   Hand-held equipment
P   Portable equipment
IT   Information technology equipment
M   Movable equipment
S   Stationary equipment

As indicated at the beginning of this Section, the intervals between inspections and tests are not mandatory. It is for each manager to decide the frequency that is right for his own particular situation. In doing so, however, he must keep in mind the fact that in the event of an accident his record of inspections and tests will be scrutinised and may be criticised.

Table 9.2   Suggested Frequencies for Inspection and Testing of Equipment

Type of premises	Type of equipment	User checks Note 1	Class I equipment Formal visual inspection Note 2	Class I equipment Inspection and test Note 3	Class II equipment Note 4 Formal visual inspection Note 2	Class II equipment Note 4 Inspection and test Note 3
Offices,	H	Before use	6 months	1 year	6 months	None
shops and	P	Weekly	1 year	2 years	2 years	None
hotels	IT	None	2 years	4 years	2 years	None
	M	Weekly	1 year	2 years	2 years	None
	S	None	2 years	4 years	2 years	None
Schools	H	Before use	4 months	6 months	1 month	1 year
	P	Weekly	4 months	6 months	1 month	1 year
	IT	Weekly	None	1 year	3 months	1 year
	M	Weekly	4 months	6 months	1 month	1 year
	S	Weekly	None	1 year	3 months	1 year
Equipment	H	Note 5	Weekly	6 months	1 month	1 year
used by the	P	Note 5	Weekly	6 months	1 month	1 year
public	IT	Note 5	Monthly	6 months	3 months	1 year
	M	Note 5	Weekly	1 year	1 month	1 year
	S	Note 5	Monthly	1 year	3 months	1 year
Industrial,	H	Before use	Monthly	6 months	3 months	6 months
including	P	Before use	Monthly	6 months	3 months	6 months
commercial	IT	Weekly	None	1 year	None	1 year
kitchens	M	Before use	Monthly	1 year	3 months	1 year
	S	Weekly	None	1 year	None	1 year
110 V	H	Weekly	Monthly	3 months	Monthly	3 months
equipment	P	Weekly	Monthly	3 months	Monthly	3 months
on construc-	IT	None	Monthly	3 months	Monthly	3 months
tion sites	M	Weekly	Monthly	3 months	Monthly	3 months
Note 6	S	None	Monthly	3months	Monthly	3months

Note 1   User checks are not recorded unless a fault is found
Note 2   When they coincide the visual inspection and the inspection and test +can be combined, but must always be recorded.
Note 3   Recording of the results of these inspections and tests is essential.
Note 4   In the event that the Class of an equipment is unknown, it must be tested as Class I.
Note 5   For some equipment, such as rides for children, daily checks are essential.
Note 6   The Table is intended to refer to equipment having a 110 V earthed centre-tapped supply. Where 230 V portable hand-held equipment is used it must be fed through a 30 mA RCD and inspections/tests must be more frequent.

The responsible manager will keep the intervals under review until a pattern of equipment failure is determined. The key factor here is the frequent inspection of their equipment by the operators. If they are successfully encouraged to take a sensible attitude to the reporting of failures and of impending failures, the periods between formal inspections and tests may be extended.

9.5   Inspection and Testing In Service

9.5.1 General

The details of the rather complicated Table 9.2 may be summarised as:

- User checks – the operator as a matter of course carries out these inspections before use. Should a fault be found it must be reported at once and logged, but no record is required where there is no fault.
- Formal visual inspections – these are more formal inspections, the results of which must be recorded.
- Combined inspections and tests. The results of these tests must be recorded, as must be the data from the tests (see Table 9.6). In many cases the impending failure of equipment can be predicted by examination of the results of measurements carried out.

9.5.2 Required Electrical Tests

To ensure the safety of users, all electrical equipments are required to undergo two electrical tests. These are:

EARTH CONTINUITY TEST

These tests only apply to Class I Equipment (see 9.3) since the others have no earth connection. Such equipments fall into two categories.

1   Those relying on the connection with earth for the safety of the user (protective earthing), and
2   Those needing a connection to earth for correct operation (functional earthing). Many electronic devices, particularly those for information technology, use filter circuits relying on the earth connection.

Either of two types of test may be carried out.

a) A continuity test with a low current tester (test currents between 20 mA and 200 mA are permissible) between the exposed metal parts of the equipment and the earth pin of the plug for a portable appliance, or the earthed terminal of a fixed wiring supply for equipment such as luminaires. The terminals should be inspected for signs of deterioration, corrosion or poor contact, and any lead should be flexed during the test, at the points of entry to the equipment and to the plug.

b) A high current continuity test at a current of no less than 1.5 times the fuse rating, with a maximum value of 25 A, for a period of between 5 and 20 seconds. An inspection of the flexible cord connections at the plug and at the equipment must also be carried out.

The measured resistance should not exceed 0.1 Ω for fixed appliances, or $(0.1 + R)\ \Omega$ for portable appliances, where R is the resistance of the protective conductor in the supply cord.

Table 9.3 provides data on the resistance of cores of flexible leads, for the value of R above.

Where the length of the lead exceeds 5 m the resistance of the protective conductor may be calculated from the data given in Table 9.3. For example if a 1.5 mm^2 lead is 13 m long, the resistance can be calculated because 13 m = 5 m + 5 m + 3 m, all lengths for which data are given, and therefore the protective conductor resistance will be:

66.5 + 66.5 + 39.9 mΩ = 172.9 mΩ or 0.1729 Ω

Flexible cords of 2.5 mm^2 and above cannot be safely connected to BS 1363 13 A plugs. For these larger sizes, industrial plugs to BS 196 or BS EN 60309-1 should be used. If a flexible cord is longer than the lengths given in Table 9.3, it should be fitted with a 30 mA RCD.

Note that information on continuity testing of other circuits will be found in Section 4.2.

INSULATION RESISTANCE TEST

For some types of appliance this test will be carried out between live conductors (phase and neutral) connected together and the body of the appliance, using an insulation resistance tester. Appliances should not be touched during the test as earthed metalwork may reach the test voltage (usually 500 V d.c.), and, whilst not dangerous (due to the internal impedance of the test instrument), it may be uncomfortable and cause danger due

Table 9.3 Resistance of Protective Conductors in Supply Cords

Conductor csa (mm²)	Conductors no./csa (mm²) (see note)	Max current (A)	Length (m)	Max length (m)	Resistance at 20°C (mΩ)
0.5	16/0.21	3.0	1.0	12	39.0
			1.5		58.5
			2.0		78.0
			2.5		97.5
			3.0		117
			4.0		156
			5.0		195
0.75	24/0.21	6.0	1.0	12	26.0
			1.5		39.0
			2.0		52.0
			2.5		65.0
			3.0		78.0
			4.0		104
			5.0		130
1.0	32/0.21	10.0	1.0	12	19.5
			1.5		29.3
			2.0		39.0
			2.5		48.8
			3.0		58.5
			4.0		78.0
			5.0		97.5
1.25	40/0.21	13.0	1.0	12	15.6
			1.5		23.4
			2.0		31.2
			2.5		39.0
			3.0		46.8
			4.0		62.4
			5.0		78.0
1.5	30/0.26	15.0	1.0	15	13.3
			1.5		20.0
			2.0		26.6
			2.5		33.3
			3.0		39.9
			4.0		53.2
			5.0		66.5
2.5	50/0.26	20.0	1.0	25	8.0
			1.5		12.0
			2.0		16.0
			2.5		20.0
			3.0		24.0
			4.0		32.0
			5.0		40.0
4.0	53/0.31	25.0	1.0	25	5.0
			1.5		7.5
			2.0		10.0
			2.5		12.5
			3.0		15.0
			4.0		20.0
			5.0		25.0

Note   Data are given in the form 'number of strands/cross sectional area of each strand'.

to involuntary movement. Before testing, the suitability of fuses should be checked and power switches placed in the ON position. The required values of insulation resistance are shown in Table 9.4. Unless information technology equipment complies with BS EN 60950 it may be damaged by this test, which should not be applied. If in doubt, DO NOT apply the test.

Note that information on insulation testing of other circuits will be found in Section 4.3.

Table 9.4   Insulation Resistance of Appliances

Appliance Class	Minimum Insulation Resistance
Class I heating, rated no greater than 3 kW	0.3 MΩ
All other Class I equipment	1.0 MΩ
Class II equipment	2.0 MΩ
Class III equipment	250 kΩ

An alternative to insulation resistance testing is the *touch current method*. Touch current is defined as the electric current that will pass through the human body when it touches one or more accessible parts of an equipment. It is measured by connecting a low current ammeter from earth to the earthed body of the appliance for Class I equipment, or to accessible surfaces of Class II equipment. The test voltage is the supply voltage, and the current must be measured within 5 seconds after the application of that voltage. Measured values must not exceed those given in Table 9.5.

The values of Table 9.5 are doubled if the appliance has no control device other than a thermal cut-out, or if the controlling thermostat or energy regulator is without an 'off' position.

Table 9.5   Maximum Permissible Touch Currents

Appliance Class	Minimum touch current
Portable or hand held Class I	0.75 mA
Class I heating appliances	0.75 mA, or 0.75 mA per kW, whichever is the greater, with a maximum of 5 mA
Other Class I equipment	3.5 mA
Class II equipment	0.25 mA
Class III equipment	0.5 mA

9.5.3 Portable Appliance Tester (PAT)

All the required tests on portable equipment can be carried out using the test equipment that has become standard for electricians. However, since these tests are now required for all items and at regular intervals, the cost of testing by a qualified electrician is considerable. Test equipment manufacturers have therefore developed a new type of instrument, known as a portable appliance tester, now universally known as a PAT. The machine is equipped with sockets to enable appliances to be plugged into it, when semi-skilled operators can subject them to the necessary tests. Although the machines are expensive, they may save a great deal of money in the long run as a result of lower labour costs.

Most of the test instrument suppliers now offer PATs as part of their range. The available equipment is very extensive, one leading manufacturer offering no less than seventeen differing PATs for various types of equipments. Many of the testers are provided with memories to enable them to record the equipment details and the results of tests; downloading to a computer is a usual facility, with software to produce test records.

For correct identification of the equipment under test, some PATs have QWERTY keyboards so that data can be inserted. More information concerning PATs will be found in the next section. Portable appliance testers (PATs) provide for the following tests:

a) Earth continuity. Often pre-set test currents up to a maximum of 25 A will be provided.

b) Insulation resistance by the applied voltage method, usually at 500 V,

In many cases PATs will offer additional test facilities such as:

c) Insulation resistance measurement by the touch current method (see 9.5.3).

d) Load test.

e) Dielectric strength test. This is seldom needed during in-service testing.

f) Earth continuity using a low value of test current. This is often called 'soft testing' and is used where damage from higher currents is a possibility.

9.6   Recording

The Electricity at Work Regulations do not actually require that a record be kept of equipment or of its inspection and testing. However, the Health and Safety Executive's Memorandum of Guidance is very clear that full records of all the equipment available and of its periodic inspection and testing should be kept. A responsible person who is investigated following an accident will have no defence at all if he is not able to produce the record of what has been done in his name. An essential pre-requisite of proper record keeping is that each separate piece of equipment is provided with an indelible and unique label to identify it.

Where a Portable Appliance Tester (PAT) is in use, it will often be the case that the label will take the form of a bar code. This has the advantage that the bar code reader of the PAT will instantly identify the piece of equipment. However, the immediate disadvantage is that the human observer will be unable to read the code. A solution is to have an indelible label that carries both the bar code and the name and letter identification details. A recent development is the introduction of a so-called "smart tag". When interrogated by a suitable PAT tester, this tag not only identifies the piece of equipment, but can also set the PAT so that the correct test is carried out on the equipment. The tags can also carry details of earlier tests, and are updated at each test. The examination of past data to recognise deterioration is thus more immediate.

It is recommended that the following records be kept.

1   A complete register of all equipment with identification details (see Table 9.1)
2   A record of formal inspections and tests (see Table 9.6).
3   A record of all equipment reported as faulty, together with reported dates (see Table 9.7).
4   A register of repairs carried out, and the dates of completion (see Table 9.8).

Table 9.7   Register of Faulty Equipment

Date	Reg. No.	Equipment fault	Location	Actioned

Table 9.6 Formal Inspections and Tests Record

Equipment Inspections and Test Record

Construction Class	Equipment type	Location		Register No.	Description
					Make
					Model
					Serial No.

	Frequency	
	Visual inspection ...... months	Inspection and test ...... months

Voltage rating V
Current rating ....A
Fuse rating ....A

Date of purchase

Guarantee details

Inspection					Test			
Date	Use	Socket	Plug	Flex	Body	Continuity	Insulation	Functional check	OK to use	Comments	Signature
						Ω √	MΩ √				

Table 9.8 Repair Register

Register number	Customer	Description	Serial number	Repairer	Suitable for return to use		
					√	Signature	Date

9.7 User Checks

It can be argued that in practice the checks by the user of the equipment are the most valuable of all. After all, the user is the person most familiar with the device because he is the one who uses it. He is likely to be in the best position to notice a change in its operation, or deterioration in its performance, as well as being more aware than others of obvious dangers such as a broken plug or a frayed lead. It is very important to impress on the user that the checks are for his own safety. In some cases, workers will continue to use equipment they know to be dangerous, especially where they feel that they will lose production (and/or money) if they stop work and report the equipment as faulty.

If a formal list of the requirements for user checks is required, it could be as follows:

1 Does the plug show signs of cracking or of overheating?
2 Does the plug have sleeved pins?
3 Is the plug fuse size correctly rated for the flexible cord and the appliance? The 3 A fuse feeds equipment with a maximum fating of 700 W and a minimum cord size of 0.5 mm², whilst the respective figures for the 13 A fuse are 3 kW and 1.25 mm².
4 Are multiway adaptors and/or extension leads in use?
5 Is the flexible lead secure in its anchorage at the plug?
6 Is the flexible lead in good condition, free from fraying, cuts or abrasion damage?
7 Is the flexible lead too long, or too short or otherwise unsatisfactory?
8 Is the flexible lead tightly bent where it exits or enters the plug or equipment?
9 Does the lead have joints? A joint in a flexible lead is considered to be very bad practice.

10 Is the flex outlet or socket outlet damaged or showing signs of overheating?

11 Is the flex outlet or socket outlet accessible to enable speedy disconnection if necessary?

12 Is the appliance working properly? Does it switch off and on correctly?

13 Is the appliance casing free from damage?

14 Can the appliance be used safely?

15 Is the equipment suitable for the environment in which it is used?

16 Are all cable runs in positions where they are unlikely to be damaged by movement of heavy equipment or of people?

17 Are all equipments requiring ventilation free from obstruction by files, papers, etc?

18 Is the equipment suitable for the work it is required to perform? Inspections and tests will not prevent damage if the equipment is not suitable for the task it is being required to carry out.

On finding faulty equipment, it must be:

1 Switched off and unplugged from the supply

2 Fitted with a label to indicate that is faulty and must not be used

3 Moved to a service area where possible

4 Reported to the responsible person.

It is vital that faulty equipment should be removed from service at once and labelled to prevent re-use. Fig. 9.1 shows equipment labels to be attached after inspection and testing.

Fig 9.1 Labels for use on equipments after testing. (a) Fail (b) Pass

Chapter 10

Lighting

10.1 Introduction

The lighting designer will seek to ensure that the system installed will provide the required illumination throughout its expected life. In most cases he will carry out measurements on the completed installation to ensure that it is performing as expected. As time goes by, the level of the light output will fall. There are two reasons for this.

1 The presence of dust and dirt on the lamps themselves and on the reflective surfaces of the luminaires will absorb some of the light so that less of it reaches the working surfaces.
2 The light output of lamps will naturally reduce with age.

These two effects can be mitigated by luminaire cleaning and by lamp replacement, the subjects of the next two Sections. The designer will have taken account of both effects, and may have stipulated regimes for luminaire cleaning and for lamp replacement. It is important that these activities are maintained. Failure to do so will lead to a fall in light output, possibly with the added disadvantage of failed or flickering lamps. This state of affairs may well lead to poor working conditions and to accidents.

10.2 Luminaire Cleaning

At first sight, cleaning does not appear to be a technical matter that need bother the maintenance manger. However, the performance of a lighting system is very dependent on the cleanliness of lamps and of reflectors. How often luminaires will need to be cleaned depends on three factors. They are:

1 The environment in which the lighting is used – dirty, normal or clean (see Table 10.1)

2 The ability of the luminaire to maintain its output. This will depend on the design of the device (see Table 10.2)

3 The allowable reduction in light output before cleaning takes place.

Table 10.1   Lighting Environment

Category	Environment	Examples
C	Clean	Offices, shops, laboratories, classrooms, etc
N	Normal	Small industrial and out-door operations, etc.
D	Dirty	Foundries, welding shops and all situations contaminated by dust, smoke, etc.

Table 10.2   Luminaire maintenance categories

Category	Description
A	Light source in free air, such as a bare GLS (general lighting service) lamp, or fluorescent tubes without diffusers or reflectors
B	A lamp in a luminaire with plated, aluminium or painted reflectors having slots at the top to create an air flow to help keep surfaces clean
C	Low bay luminaires with reflectors, plus as for B but without air flow slots
D	Recessed luminaires
E	Surface modular and general diffusing luminaires
F	Uplighters

The ability of a lamp/luminaire combination to prevent the build-up of dirt and of dust will depend very much on its design. Table 10.2 classifies a number of standard designs, giving each a maintenance category.

The next matter to consider is the luminaire maintenance factor (LMF). This factor takes account of the deterioration in light output as the luminaire becomes dirty or dusty. There is no intention here to take account of the normal deterioration of lamp output with age. It is defined as:

$$\text{LMF} = \frac{\text{light output after a specified time}}{\text{initial light output}}$$

The value of the LMF will clearly depend on the cleanliness of the environment, the time interval between luminaire cleaning operations and the type of luminaire. Suggested values for LMF in various situations are given in Table 10.3.

For example, consider that the design illuminance for a drawing office lit by fluorescent fittings with reflectors having air slots is 600 lux. If we need to determine what the illuminance may become if the luminaires are cleaned every three years, we proceed as follows.

A drawing office can be assumed to be a clean situation (lighting environment C from Table 10.1)

The fluorescent fittings with slotted reflectors are category B from Table 10.2.

From Table 10.3 we can look up the luminaire maintenance factor (LMF) for a category B luminaire with a three-year cleaning interval in a clean environment as 0.79.

Hence the illuminance is expected to fall to:

original illuminance × LMF

which is: 600 × 0.79 = 474 lux.

The answer to low luminance levels due to dirty luminaires is really to start with a higher level in the first place, but often this is beyond the competence of the maintenance manager. So what can be done from a maintenance point of view if the illuminance falls too low? The answer is to clean the luminaires more often.

Cleaning must be properly and effectively carried out. An abrasive cleaner may appear to give fast results the first time it is used, but may well scratch painted and aluminium surfaces, making future cleaning more difficult as well as degrading the lighting performance of the system. It is as well to seek the advice of the luminaire manufacturer. If this is not forthcoming, lamps and reflectors should be thoroughly washed in a warm soapy solution, then rinsed and air-dried. Louvres are always difficult to clean. Perhaps the most effective method is to remove and wash them in warm water. Specular louvres are particularly difficult to clean, and should only be installed in very clean situations.

Care in handling plastics is essential, because some types become very brittle with age. Some will yellow very badly as time passes, reducing their light-transmitting properties. It is important to appreciate that the walls and ceiling of the situation concerned are also reflectors, their performance being reduced by dust and dirt. Regular cleaning of such surfaces is essential.

There is no reason why cleaning must be carried out by skilled electricians. BS 7671 makes it clear that 'instructed persons' can be used, but the maintenance manager must make sure that they are aware of the dangers posed and luminaires must be switched off before maintenance begins.

Table 10.3 Luminaire maintenance factors

Luminaire Category (Table 10.2)	0.5			1.0			1.5			2.0			2.5			3.0		
Environment (Table 10.1)	C	N	D	C	N	D	C	N	D	C	N	D	C	N	D	C	N	D
A	0.95	0.92	0.88	0.93	0.89	0.83	0.91	0.87	0.80	0.89	0.84	0.78	0.87	0.82	0.75	0.85	0.79	0.73
B	0.95	0.91	0.89	0.90	0.86	0.83	0.87	0.83	0.79	0.84	0.80	0.75	0.82	0.76	0.71	0.79	0.74	0.68
C	0.93	0.89	0.83	0.89	0.81	0.72	0.84	0.74	0.64	0.80	0.69	0.59	0.77	0.64	0.54	0.74	0.61	0.52
D	0.92	0.87	0.83	0.88	0.82	0.77	0.85	0.79	0.73	0.83	0.77	0.71	0.81	0.75	0.68	0.79	0.73	0.65
E	0.96	0.93	0.91	0.94	0.90	0.86	0.92	0.88	0.83	0.91	0.86	0.81	0.90	0.85	0.80	0.90	0.84	0.79
F	0.92	0.89	0.85	0.86	0.81	0.74	0.81	0.73	0.65	0.77	0.66	0.57	0.73	0.60	0.51	0.70	0.55	0.45

Years between cleanings

10.3   Lamp Replacement

It is generally understood that lamps will not last forever, and that they must be changed. There are two ways of looking at lamp replacement. The first is to adopt a policy of changing each lamp as it fails (often called 'spot replacement'). Whilst this method gives the more efficient lighting, it is extremely expensive, as labour and, often, time-consuming access equipment, is necessary every time a failure occurs. The alternative is planned replacement, where all lamps are changed following a predetermined pattern. The problems with this method are that the lighting is likely to deteriorate prior to re-lamping due to failed lamps, and that units, which are still likely to have many hours of effective life, are changed.

Three factors must be considered before arriving at the interval for planned lamp replacement. They are:

1　The proportion of the lamps still operating after a specified burning time. This is known as the **'lamp survival factor'** or LSF.

3　The proportion of the initial light output of the lamps after a specified time in operation. This ageing effect is taken into account using the **'lamp lumen maintenance factor'** or LLMF.

3　The cleaning frequency of the lamps.

10.3.1 Lamp Survival Factor (LSF)

No lamp will last forever, although the recently introduced induction lamp is claimed to have an operating life in excess of 50,000 hours. Different types of lamp can be expected to operate for differing lengths of time, as is shown in Table 10.4. Lamps will need to be changed when their light output falls to an unacceptably low level, or when the proportion of failed or flickering lamps has a distracting effect on installation users. The use of electronic starter switches in fluorescent and other discharge lamps will often cure the problem of flickering – the starter switches off the lamp if flickering occurs. Spot replacement of lamps will depend on the situation. For example, two failed lamps in widely separated positions in a workshop may well be tolerable, but are unlikely to be so in an office.

These figures must be used with care. They are typical, but lamps in particular batches from a manufacturer may well give shorter or longer life times.

10.3.2 Lamp Luminance Maintenance Factor (LLMF)

It is important to appreciate that this factor is not the same as the luminaire maintenance factor (LMF), since it is concerned with the reduction in the

Table 10.4   Typical Lamp Survival Hours

Type of lamp	Proportion of lamps surviving after given time (thousands of hours)											
	0.1	0.5	1.0	1.5	2.0	4.0	6.0	8.0	10.0	14.0	18.0	22.0
Filament (GLS)	1.00	0.98	0.50	0.30								
Fluorescent	1.00	1.00	1.00	1.00	1.00	1.00	0.99	0.95	0.85	0.75	0.64	0.50
Metal halide	1.00	1.00	0.97	0.96	0.95	0.93	0.91	0.87	0.83	0.70	0.50	
Mercury	1.00	1.00	1.00	1.00	0.99	0.98	0.97	0.95	0.92	0.84	0.75	0.59
High pressure sodium	1.00	1.00	1.00	1.00	0.99	0.98	0.96	0.94	0.92	0.85	0.75	0.60

output of the lamp due to ageing (not the luminaire due to increasing dirt). Cleaning has no effect on the light luminance maintenance factor.

This factor can be defined as:

$$\text{LLMF} = \frac{\text{light output after a specified operating time}}{\text{initial light output}}$$

Typical values of LLMF for various lamps are given in Table 10.5.

Table 10.5   Typical Lamp Lumen Maintenance Factors

Type of lamp	Proportion of light output after given time (thousands of hours)											
	0.1	0.5	1.0	1.5	2.0	4.0	6.0	8.0	10.0	14.0	18.0	22.0
Filament (GLS)	1.00	0.97	0.93	0.89								
Fluorescent multiphosphor	1.00	0.98	0.96	0.95	0.94	0.91	0.87	0.86	0.85	0.83		
Fluorescent halophosphate	1.00	0.97	0.94	0.91	0.89	0.83	0.80	0.78	0.76	0.72		
Metal halide	1.00	0.96	0.93	0.90	0.87	0.78	0.72	0.69	0.66	0.60	0.52	
Mercury	1.00	0.99	0.97	0.95	0.93	0.87	0.80	0.76	0.72	0.64	0.58	0.53
High pressure sodium	1.00	1.00	0.98	0.97	0.96	0.93	0.91	0.89	0.88	0.86	0.83	0.81

10.3.3 Frequency of Lamp Cleaning

It follows that labour will be saved if lamps are replaced instead of cleaning them. This is not to say that lamp cleaning is not necessary. The following example will indicate the steps to be taken in determining a sensible period at which lamps should be changed.

Consider a high bay assembly area which is lit by high pressure sodium lamps. We first have to decide on acceptable minimum levels of lamp survival factor (LSF) and of lamp lumen maintenance factor (LLMF). These decisions will depend on how low we are prepared to allow the lighting level to become before replacement.

Assume that we decide that an LSF of 0.94 and an LLMF of 0.85 are the minimum acceptable figures. From Table 10.4 we see that the LSF for these lamps at 8000 hours is 0.94, and Table 10.5 we obtain a figure of 0.86 for 14000 hours. It thus follows that replacement should be at 8000 hours. Assuming a working day of 8 hours and five days per week for 49 weeks per year, the lamps will be running for

$$8 \times 5 \times 49 = 1960 \text{ hours per year.}$$

Thus the lamp replacement must take place every $\dfrac{8000}{1960}$ years, or 4 years approximately.

After an estimation of cleaning times for lamps, replacement can be scheduled to coincide with cleaning.

10.4   Disposal of Old Lamps

The main hazard with all lamps is due to the fracture of the glass bulb. In the event of accidental breakage, it is important that the glass is safely collected for disposal. Special precautions are necessary with low-pressure sodium lamps, and are described later. The best option is usually to place failed or removed lamps in the packaging from which their replacements have been taken. If large quantities are concerned, special fragmentation machines are available, but must be used only by trained staff.

Sodium is a dangerous material that will burn when it comes into contact with water due to the emission of hydrogen. High-pressure sodium lamps contain very little of this material, which is, in any case, enclosed in the almost-unbreakable arc tube. Low-pressure sodium lamps must be broken with great care and flooded with water until the sodium has burned away. The water is best added from a distance with a hose. The mercury contained in fluorescent and high-pressure mercury lamps is toxic, and disposal of large numbers of broken lamps, (at one of their licensed sites), should be discussed with the Local Authority.

See also Chapter 13, Waste Disposal, and particularly Section 13.3, Disposal of Discharge Lamps. Useful guidance can be found in Department of the Environment publication 'Disposal of Discharge Lamps', LAC 34/2.

Chapter 11

Electromagnetic Compatibility

11.1 What is electromagnetic interference?

A cable sets up a magnetic field when it carries current. Any change in this current results in a corresponding change in the intensity of the electromagnetic field. Since the field spreads out from the cable, it is likely to embrace conductors of other systems; any change in the electromagnetic field intensity will induce an e.m.f. (voltage) in these conductors. This voltage may affect the operation of the system in which it is induced. It is called electromagnetic interference (EMI), Where there is no harmful electromagnetic interference, the two systems are electromagnetically compatible.

The above suggests that all electromagnetic interference is generated by changing magnetic fields which induce e.m.f.s. This is far from the truth. Often the interference will be 'imported' into the installation by way of mains-borne disturbances, such as transients due to lightning, switching, etc., waveform disturbances and so on.

Many maintenance managers who are well aware of dangers associated with traditional technologies may not appreciate those due to the introduction of electronic technologies. For example a manufacturer may use a programmable logic controller (PLC) to control a machine or a process. If the operation of the PLC is compromised by the nearby use of a walkie-talky or by a voltage transient on the mains supply, the controlled machine may well behave in an unintended manner, giving rise to safety problems.

All maintenance managers cannot fail to be aware of the enormous growth of electronic controls, especially the application of digital technologies. Whilst such devices bring many benefits, including increased functionality, they also suffer from reliability and performance problems. One of these problems is electro-magnetic interference. All electronic devices emit EM disturbances that may interfere with the correct operation of other electronic equipment. The control of emissions of, and immunity to, EM disturbances in all electrical and electronic equipment is known as electromagnetic compatibility (EMC). It is very important that the equipment designer makes all necessary information available to the manufacturer, the installer, the operator, and, of course, the maintenance manager, to make sure that the intended EMC protection methods are implemented and maintained to ensure that the intended levels of emissions are not increased.

It is most important to appreciate that reliance must not be placed on the use of CE marked equipment (see page viii) that complies with EMC Directive 5. The directive makes no pretence to deal with safety, and in many cases CE marked equipment will fail to comply with EMC requirements, particularly in the event of faults, operator errors, misuse, and maintenance situations. It must be appreciated that certain maintenance operations, such as the removal of covers, gaskets and so on, are likely the increase electro-magnetic emissions; it is vital that such items are properly replaced on completion of the operation, where necessary new components being supplied to maintain the original integrity.

In the vast majority of cases, interference occurs as a result of the way in which the installation and equipment were constructed, and is thus outside the competence of the maintenance manager. The induced voltage (and hence the level of interference) actually depends on the rate of change of the linking magnetic flux, and hence on the rate of change of the inducing current (di/dt). It is thus at its maximum when current changes are very rapid, as in lightning strikes, starting of large machinery, switching, installation faults, waveforms of currents in electrical cables suddenly switched by solid state equipment, and so on.

Another problem can arise from interference due to electrostatic fields. These fields are due to the voltage carried by a cable, and are known as electrostatic interference (ESI).

11.2 Controlling Electro-magnetic Compatibility

The maintenance manager must be aware that whenever electrical and electronic technologies are used in control or protection, risks to health and safety may result from errors and malfunctions due to a lack of adequate electromagnetic compatibility (EMC). To control EMC-related functional safety, assessments must be made of hazards and risks. Whilst these will not be the sole prerogative of the maintenance manager, he must be aware of them and ensure that they are maintained during operations for which he is responsible. The following must be considered:

1 To what electromagnetic disturbances might the equipment be exposed?

2 What will be the effects of these disturbances on the equipment?

3 How might possible EM disturbances emitted by the equipment affect others?

4 What are the safety implications of these disturbances?

5 What level of proof is required to ensure that action has been taken to make sure that safety will not be impaired?

The answers to these questions, along with the answers to them and the actions that result, must be fully documented.

The Institution of Electrical Engineers has issued a comprehensive Guidance Document 'EMC and Functional Safety' which is available for downloading from their website..

11.3 Avoiding EMI

Generally speaking, the maintenance manager will have little control over the construction of the electrical installation for which he is responsible. To give a list of the steps to be considered during construction to avoid EMI may therefore seem pointless. However, if the maintenance manager is aware of the factors which may give rise to the problem, he is more likely to be able to alleviate it should it occur.

Some of the steps to be followed to avoid EMI are as follows:

1 Use a clean earth connection where possible. This is a dedicated direct earth connection from the sensitive equipment directly to the main earthing terminal, its run ideally following closely that of the phase and neutral conductors

2 Identify possible sources of interference and keep them separated from sensitive equipment or circuitry

3 Fit surge protectors and filters in the power supplies to sensitive systems

4 When designing a new wiring system, avoid loops that set up strong magnetic fields (induction loops)

5 Always used screened or twisted pair cables in telecommunications or data circuits

6 Make sure that equipment in use meets the emission standard BS EN 50081 or the immunity standard BS EN 50082

7 Ensure that bonding connections are kept as short as possible

8 Screen sensitive equipments and bond metal enclosures

9 Bond metal pipes and screens between cables

10 Separate power and signal cables, trying to avoid parallel runs (see Table 11.1). Where they must cross, arrange for them to do so at right angles

11 Keep sensitive equipment away from circuits feeding heavy and changing currents to equipments such as lift motors

12 Tripping of circuits under fault conditions often is unavoidable. However, it may be minimised by selection of device characteristics and by introducing time delays

13 Avoid the use of systems with combined neutral and earth connections (TN-C, usually earthed concentric systems)

14 If possible, arrange for all metal service pipes to enter the premises at a common position

15 Ideally, single-core cables should be individually enclosed in earthed metal. In practice this is usually impracticable because of the heavy circulating currents which result due to induced e.m.f. after they are bonded together

16 Where two communications systems that have separate earthing, any link between then should ideally be non-electrical, i.e. fibre optic.

Table 11.1 suggests the minimum separation from cables with the stated voltage and current levels to avoid EMI as far as is possible.

Table 11.1 Power and signal cables separation

Power cable current (A)	Minimum separation (m)	Power cable voltage (V)	Minimum separation (m)
5	0.24	115	0.25
15	0.35	240	0.45
50	0.50	415	0.58
100	0.60	3300	1.10
300	0.85	6600	1.25
600	1.05	11000	1.40

11.4 Data processing and telecommunications equipment and circuits

These are the systems that are most likely to be affected by electromagnetic interference. They are widespread, and there can be few organisations that do not make use of them. Interference with these systems can be very serious indeed, interrupting communications and corrupting data. The maintenance manager should give careful attention to the matter, particularly the information contained in BS 6701: 1994 Code of Practice for the Installation of Apparatus Intended for Connection to Telecommunication Systems.

Chapter 12

Lightning Conductor Systems

12.1 Installation design

Lightning is the discharge to earth of very high voltage charges that build up in clouds under certain conditions. The current in a discharge is variable, but may be very high indeed. If the discharge passes through a building on its way to earth, that building is likely to be mechanically damaged, the heat from the discharge often also resulting in fire.

A very important problem arises following a lightning strike to, or in the vicinity of, an installation. The exceedingly high rates of change of current are likely to have considerable deleterious effects on some equipment within the installation, especially on electronics based systems. These effects have been considered at greater length in Chapter 11.

A lightning conductor system is designed and installed to attempt to prevent this from happening. It provides a conducting path to earth from the finials, pointed rods mounted at the highest points of the building, to electrodes buried in, or driven into, the ground. The lightning conductors themselves usually take the form of large cross-section copper tape.

BS 6651: 1992 Code of Practice for the Protection of Structures against Lightning gives advice on the subject, dealing with the need for protection, design, inspection, testing and records.

12.2 Inspecting and testing

Inspection and testing of the lightning protection system must be carried out at intervals that do not exceed 12 months. Additionally, inspection and testing must be carried out following a known lightning strike to the installation.

12.2.1 Inspection

The continuity of all protective conductors must be confirmed, together with the fact that the installation complies fully with the record drawings (see 12.3 that follows). Of particular importance is an inspection to verify that all earthing connections are in good order and that no signs of corrosion are present. Changes in the structure of the building must be noted, and advice taken on the possible need to extend the lightning protection system. This is of particular importance where the change involves the erection of any system that rises above the previous building height, such as an aerial, mast, chimney, etc.

12.2.2 Testing

Before carrying out any testing of the lightning conductor system it is very important to ensure that it has not become live due to a fault involving another system.

The testing required will consist of measuring the resistance to earth of each earth electrode, after disconnecting it from the lightning conductor system. Detailed information on completion of these tests can be found in Section 4.6. The British Standard makes clear that the total resistance of the complete electrode system (which may well comprise of a number of electrodes) should never exceed 10 Ω. Effectively, all the electrodes are interconnected, and are thus in parallel with each other. Thus, the maximum resistance to earth of an individual electrode must never exceed 10 times the number of electrodes. If, for example, there are eight electrodes, the resistance of any one of them must not exceed 8 x 10 Ω or 80 Ω. It will be appreciated that, in this case, eight resistors, each of 80 Ω and connected in parallel, will have a combined resistance of 10 Ω. Should the resistance to earth of individual electrodes be less than 80 Ω, then the overall resistance to earth will be less than 10 Ω and hence the system will be safer.

The resistance to earth of an electrode is very much affected by environmental conditions. For example, an electrode surrounded by wet soil will have a lower resistance to earth than will an identical electrode surrounded by dry earth. It is therefore of paramount importance when testing to note the conditions prevailing at the time. As with all forms of testing, it is useful to compare results with those of earlier tests. If, for example, electrode resistance is higher than previously, it can be seen that this may be due to it being dryer at present than was the case at the time of the earlier test. It is foolish to achieve lower test results by watering the surrounds of an electrode, and this must never be done.

12.3   Recording

The following information applying to the lightning conductor system must be recorded in a book or on a computer file kept for the purpose.

1 Complete sets of scale drawings for the lightning protection installation. If changes are made, the drawings must be suitably amended
2 Details of the type and position of every earth electrode.
3 Data concerning the expected soil resistivity expressed in Ωm.
4 The results of all previous tests, each with completion date and environmental conditions (such as the dampness of the soil).
5 Full data on the action taken on the results of tests, including completion dates.

This record must be always available for inspection. As mentioned previously, the information in this record would be valuable to the maintenance engineer following an occurrence, such as a fire following a lightning strike.

12.4   Bonding

All incoming services, such as electricity, gas and water, must be bonded together at their point of entry to the building and to the lightning protection system.

Where an installation is supplied with electrical energy by the use of low voltage overhead lines, additional protection is required by BS 7671 where the incidence of lightning exceeds 25 thunderstorm days per year. Since the records show that nowhere in the UK has more than 20 thunderstorm days per year, such measures are not needed here.

Chapter 13

Waste Disposal

13.1. Special Waste Regulations 1996

The European Council Hazardous Waste Directive 91/689/EEC is implemented by the Special Waste Regulations 1996. If waste is in categories covered by Schedules 2, 3 or 4 is concerned, it becomes "special waste" and is subject to these controls. These waste definitions are complex, but effectively they cover materials that can be considered as:

1	Explosive	detonates under specific conditions
2	Oxidising	combines with oxygen
3	Flammable or highly flammable	burns easily
4	Irritant	causes physical irritation
5	Toxic	disease causing
6	Carcinogenic	cancer causing
7	Corrosive	causing corrosion
8	Infectious	communicates disease
9	Teratogenic	may give rise to birth defects
10	Mutagenic	may cause genetic changes
11	Release toxic gases	emits gases which may cause disease
12	Ecotoxic.	may cause disease in living organisms

The Special Waste Regulations require the implementation of a system which ensures that all substances which will, when their life is finished, become special waste, are documented and traceable from the time of entry to the site until they leave it.

Generally the characteristics of materials that fall into this category are given below. The list is not exhaustive.

1 Materials that have a low flashpoint
2 Carcinogenic substances (those which may possibly cause cancer)
3 Corrosive substances such as acids
4 Irritant substances

13.2.   Disposal of capacitors

Polychlorinated biphenyls (PCBs) were widely used until 1976 as cooling liquid in power transformers and capacitors. The chemical is very toxic (hazard classification N), particularly to aquatic life, so correct disposal is essential. They may still be found in power factor correction capacitors, both those used for bulk correction and types connected for individual correction of motors, fluorescent fittings and so on. There is no labelling on these capacitors to indicate the contents.

Capacitors containing PCBs can continue in use so long as the case is serviceable, but leaks are likely to occur eventually. A brown stain usually indicates a leak. To dispose of such a capacitor, the operative must use heavy duty polythene (not rubber) gloves, which must be bagged up in a sealed container with the capacitor and any material used to clean the surroundings; such a container can usually be disposed of with normal waste.

If the capacitor is from one of a number of similar luminaires, the probability is that all were installed at the same time, meaning that all the capacitors are the same age. It would be wise to replace all the capacitors to circumvent future problems. Since the use of PCBs in capacitors was banned in 1986, it follows that the luminaires must be old. Rather than replace the capacitors, it may be worth considering renewal of all the luminaires. Very big efficiency improvements in fluorescent luminaires over the last few years may well mean that replacing them will be a cost effective, as well as a safety effective, move.

13.3.   Disposal of discharge lamps

13.3.1 Fluorescent Lamps

There is no danger, other than that of broken glass, with this type of lamp. The widespread belief that the fluorescent powder that coats the inside of the tube is dangerous has no substance. Small numbers of fluorescent tubes may be disposed of as normal waste. Where large numbers are involved (after bulk lamp changing), the use of lamp crushers is recommended. The resulting waste should be treated with water and the Local Authority consulted concerning disposal.

13.3.2 Mercury Lamps

No special precautions are necessary here. However, very small amounts of mercury vapour may be released when tubes are broken, and reference to the Department of the Environment guidance 'Disposal of Discharge Lamps' 34/2 is recommended. Fragmentation followed by copious irrigation with water is recommended.

13.3.3 Sodium Lamps

Sodium is a very dangerous substance, largely because it will burn in the presence of water. High-pressure sodium lamps contain only very small amounts of the material, and since it is enclosed in an inner arc tube that is very difficult to break, there is no problem in disposal.

Low-pressure sodium lamps, however, contain comparatively large quantities of sodium contained in an easily broken tube. The special steps needed for disposal are considered in Section 10.4.

13.4. Disposal of other equipment

The electrical maintenance manager will find the need to dispose of other waste materials, and information on the most usual is as follows.

13.4.1 Transformers

Transformers often include a coolant, which may well be PCB. Their disposal will follow the steps mentioned in Section 13.2 for capacitors. However, in the case of a large power transformer, the quantity of PCB present may be such as to require its incineration in a special furnace, the location and details of which can be obtained from the local Health and Safety Executive.

13.4.2 Oil-filled Transformers

Waste oil from a power transformer is scheduled as hazardous waste, and must be disposed of in co-operation with the Local Waste Authority in accordance with the requirements of the Hazardous Waste Directive and the Special Waste Regulations.

13.4.3 Asbestos

Asbestos is common in electrical equipments as well as in building construction. It is known to be a carcinogen (a material causing cancer) and as such is a special waste material. Expert advice should be sought, usually from the local aiuthority, as to its safe disposal.

Chapter 14

Legionnaire's Disease

14.1   What is Legionnaire's Disease?

Legionella pneumophila is a bacterium found in water sprays. If inhaled in a water droplet or as the particles left after a droplet has evaporated, it can cause fatal pneumonia in people whose resistance is weakened by smoking, their age, existing illness and so on. Such infections are given the general name legionellosis. Where outbreaks have occurred they have been traced to infection in water systems, particularly in cooling towers.

The Health and Safety Commission has produced a publication 'Legionnaire's Disease. The control of legionella bacteria in water systems' which is an approved Code of Practice and Guidance. It covers in very great detail the control of legionella in water systems and should be on the bookshelf of every maintenance manager. The HSE guidance note HS(G)70 'The Control of Legionellosis including Legionnaire's Disease' is also useful for the maintenance manager, as is their 'Legionnaires disease – a guide for employers', IAC27.

14.2   Legal Framework

The Health and Safety at Work, etc. Act, 1974 and the Control of Substances Hazardous to Health Regulations, 1994 require that measures are taken to reduce or prevent the risk from exposure to Legionellae. They include the need for:

1   Minimising or preventing the risk from exposure
2   Identifying and assessing the risk
3   Record keeping
4   Training, selection and management of employees
5   Responsibilities of installers, suppliers, designers, manufacturers, and so on

14.3   Water Systems

The legislation outlined in the previous Section applies to any premises or work activity where water is used or stored and where water droplets may be created and inhaled. It is difficult to think of a normal work situation where these conditions do NOT apply. Experience shows that the following present a risk of legionellosis.

1   Any plant or system containing water at more than 20°C which may release a spray during operation or during maintenance works
2   Water systems including a cooling tower.
3   Water systems that include an evaporative condenser.
4   Spa baths and whirlpools.
5   Shower heads.
6   Air washes and humidifiers, particularly where there is a water spray at a temperature of more than 20°C.
7   Water services of any size situated in places where the residents are susceptible, like old persons' homes, nursing homes, and so on.

14.4   Risk Control

Where it is considered that there is a risk of legionellosis the use of water systems should be suspended as far as possible until a scheme to control the risk has been implemented. Such a scheme must include:

1   A full description of the safe operation of the plant concerned
2   A complete layout plan of the plant
3   Details of the precautions to be taken.

Precautions to reduce risk should include:

1   Making sure that both the system and the water in it are clean
2   Changing the water periodically to avoid stagnation
3   Reducing the release of water sprays
4   Introducing a regime to ensure safe operation and maintenance
5   Where possible to ensure that water temperatures do not exceed 20°C
6   To ensure that the water system is free of materials that harbour bacteria or provide nutrients for their growth

14.5 Record Keeping

Where an assessment has shown that there is a possible risk of Legionellosis, a person who has responsibility for implementation of precautions must be appointed. He must keep records, which will include:

1 The assessment of risk, with full details of the person who carried out the assessment
2 The name and position of the person responsible for managing the risk
3 A detailed scheme for elimination of the risk
4 The names and positions of the persons responsible for implementing the scheme
5 Details of how the scheme is managed
6 Details of plant systems in use and of their current state
7 Details of precautionary measures taken, by whom and when
8 Results of tests and inspections with dates and identification of the staff responsible
9 If and when remedial work is needed, details of when and by whom it was carried out.

There is no specific legal requirement for this record keeping, but the responsible person would be in a very difficult position after an incident if he were not able to produce the records.

Chapter 15

Risk Assessment and Manual Handling

15.1 Risk assessment

This is a difficult subject for the maintenance manger to face, particularly if it is new to him. How does he assess risk? What activities are concerned? Which personnel must be assessed?

The Management of Health and Safety at Work Regulations provide the answers to these questions, but always in a general way that may be difficult to apply to the particular circumstances prevailing. There are five Regulations particularly applying to maintenance.

15.1.1 Regulation 3(1)

The employer must make an assessment of the risks to the health and safety of his employees, as well as to others who may be on the premises but are not his employees. He needs to identify the measures needed to comply with the statutory provisions.

15.1.2 Regulation 4(1)

The employer must identify and put into operation arrangements for the planning, organisation, control, monitoring and review of protective and preventive measures that will ensure the health and safety of all at the work site.

15.1.3 Regulation 5

Where there are risks to employees due to their exposure to extreme temperatures, exposure to chemicals, to radiation, to infections, etc. the employer must implement health surveillance procedures.

15.1.4 Regulation 6

Competent persons must be employed to assist compliance with the Regulations. In some instances, this will mean the employment of specialists.

15.1.5 Regulation 7

Procedures must be established where possible to deal with particular risks. Such risks include bomb alarms, accidents, fire and the leakage of hazardous substances.

Risk assessment must only be carried out by those competent to do so. Any employee, who is required to carry out such work but doubts his ability to do it, must at once inform his employer.

Steps taken in risk assessment are:

1 Identification of the hazard
2 Identification of those who may suffer harm
3 Careful evaluation of existing precautions
4 Recording of the findings. Table 15.1 shows a typical form.
5 Implementation of the recommendations
6 A review of the assessment.

Table 15.1 Risk Assessment Form

Risk Assessment		Location		Assessor		
				Date		
				Review on		
Hazard list	Persons at risk	Controls in place	Risks not controlled	Record of action taken		
					Date	Action

Items to be covered in each column of the form include:

RISK ASSESSMENT

Low and high temperatures, manual handling, noise, tripping and slipping, moving parts, vehicle movements, chemicals, fire, ejection of material such as steam or mouldings, work height, wiring, fumes, gases, dusts, lighting levels, pressurised systems, etc.

PERSONS AT RISK

Must include both those doing the work and those affected by the work.

CONTROLS IN PLACE

Has the risk been reduced as far as possible? Are the precautions taken, such as barriers, guards, protective clothing, training, signs, etc., adequate?

RISKS NOT CONTROLLED

Describe the recommended actions for risks not properly controlled. State risk priorities in terms of the hazard and the numbers of persons concerned.

15.2 Manual Handling

Made under the Health and Safety at Work etc. Act 1974 and implemented by the European Directive 90/269/EEC, the Manual Handling Operations Regulations 1992 came into force in 1993. Manual Handling Reference L23, published by the Health and Safety Executive, provides guidance for safety management.

The employer is required to avoid the need for employees to undertake manual handling where this could involve the risk of their injury. There will be situations where this is not possible. In such cases, the employer is required to assess the operations following the factors listed in Table 15.2 (taken from the Manual Handling Operations Regulations) and to answer the questions posed. He is then required to take such actions as will reduce the risk of injury.

Table 15.2   Schedule of Manual Handling Operations

Factors	Questions
The tasks	Do they involve: 1 holding or moving loads away from the body? 2 body movements such as stooping, reaching up or twisting? 3 excessive load movement, including lifting, lowering or carrying? 4 excessive pushing or pulling of loads? 5 sudden movement of loads? 6 prolonged or frequent physical effort? 7 insufficient rest or recovery periods?
The loads	Are they heavy, bulky unwieldy, difficult to grasp, with contents likely to shift, sharp, hot?
The environment	Are there: 1 uneven, slippery or unstable floors? 2 variations in floor or work surfaces? 3 poor lighting conditions? 4 space constraints that prevent good posture? 5 extremes of humidity or temperature? 6 poor ventilation or gusts of wind?
Capability	Does the work: 1 require unusual attributes such as strength or height? 2 create a hazard to those who may have a health problem? 3 require special training or information?
Other factors	Is posture or movement hindered by protective equipment or by clothing?

Chapter 16

Safety Signals and Signs

16.1 Introduction

The Health and Safety (Safety Signs and Signals) Regulations 1966 set the minimum requirements for the provision of safety signs at work by European Council Directive 92/58/EEC. Emergency escape and exit signs have been considered in Chapter 7. These signs no longer contain text, thus making them universally recognisable in all countries. The Health and Safety Executive has published guidance to the Regulations in its publication L64.

Whilst the provision of these signs is not the direct responsibility of the maintenance manager, it is of the greatest importance that he is aware of them so that he can ensure that they are kept in good condition.

16.2 Sign Colours

The colours specified for the various signs are shown in Table 16.1, which is taken from Schedule 1 of the Regulations. Guidance on a wider range of signs will be found in HSE document L64.

16.3 Signs

European Union signs do not use words so that they are international.

See inside back cover for examples of these signs.

Clearly, the size and position of all these signs is important; postage-stamp size signs mounted a metre above floor level will not gain attention. All signs should be positioned between 2 m and 2.5 m above the floor level. The size of the sign depends on the maximum distance from which it is to be viewed, and the following formula applies.

$$A = \frac{L^2}{2000}$$ where A is the area of the sign in m² and L is the distance from which it is to be viewed in m.

Table 16.1   Colours for safety signs

Colour	Purpose of sign	Information and instructions
Red	Prohibition sign	Dangerous behaviour
	Danger alarm	Shutdown, stop, emergency cutouts. Evacuate
	Fire fighting equipment	Location and identification
Yellow or amber	Warning sign	Take care and precautions
Blue	Mandatory sign	Wear protective equipment
		Specific action or behaviour required
Green	First aid and emergency escape signs	Routes, exits, doors, facilities, equipment Return to normal
	No danger	

Assuming a viewing distance (L) of 10 m, $A = \dfrac{10^2}{2000} = \dfrac{100}{2000} = 0.05 \text{ m}^2$

This means that a square sign would need to be 22.4 cm × 22.4 cm in this instance.

16.4   Notices and Identification

BS 7671, Requirements for Electrical Installations (more often recognised as the 16th Edition of the IEE Wiring Regulations) requires a large number of labels. They include:

1 Switch or control gear identification,
2 To identify bonding conductor and earth electrode connections,
3 Isolators identification,
4 Fuses identification,
5 Circuit breakers identification,
6 Positions of buried cables,
7 Switches for mechanical maintenance identification,
8 Fireman's switch identification,
9 Periodic inspection and testing dates,
10 Testing of residual current devices,
11 Identification of areas reserved for skilled or instructed persons,
12 Identification of earth-free locations,

13 Identification of areas protected by electrical separation,
14 Presence of voltages exceeding 250 V

The identification colours for conduits and other pipes are as shown in Table 16.2.

Table 16.2 Colours for identifying the contents of pipes	
Pipe contents	*Colour*
Electrical services	Orange
Ventilation ducts	Orange
Water	Green
Steam	Silver-grey
Oils	Brown
Gases	Yellow ochre
Acids and alkalis	Violet
Air	Light blue
Other liquids	Black

Index